MY FRIENDS
THE DOCTORS

MY FRIENDS THE DOCTORS

BY

Sigmund L Wilens MD

═══════

NEW YORK

ATHENEUM

1961

CONTENTS

MY FRIENDS
THE DOCTORS

1

With Much Sadness and Some Irritation

T H E old adage that dead men tell no tales does not hold true as far as the medical profession is concerned. Dead men have for centuries been telling doctors the story of how they got sick and why they died, and doctors have made use of this information very effectively in the treatment of other sick people. This story can be unfolded only by anatomical dissection after death, a procedure that is generally called an autopsy and, by purists, a necropsy. The public owes to the dissectors of the dead a debt that it has seldom recognized or acknowledged.

I am the kind of doctor who specializes in performing autopsies, and I am known as a pathologist. In recent years the public has come to learn a great deal about the various species of doctors and can tell the difference, let us say, between an ophthalmologist and a radiologist without too much difficulty, but it knows precious little about the habits, customs and usages of pathologists.

The average person seldom meets a pathologist, at least while he is still alive. Even if he has a close friend or two who are pathologists, he generally has only vague ideas as to what they do and why they do it. Pathologists as a rule find it wise to avoid discussing the subject, partly because it involves lengthy and complicated explanations, and partly because such conversations tend to become morbid. Death and the circumstances immediately surrounding it do not make very agreeable topics of casual conversation. Occasionally curious-minded persons will persist in probing a pathologist about his work. Soon, however, some more sensible person in the group will say, "Let's talk about something more pleasant." And so pathologists are doctors who have been content to avoid attention because they realize that there is a degree of taboo about their work.

Most people seem to have acquired their sketchy impressions about pathologists from murder mysteries, television plays and other fictionalized accounts in which post-mortem examinations are involved. Medical examiners and regular pathologists can be regarded as kissing kin. The ordinary pathologist is concerned with natural causes of death. Medical examiners are pathologists who specialize in the study of death due to

4

violence. The distinction between the two is seldom made in fictional accounts, and in truth there is much overlapping in the activities of the two groups.

In the mystery story, the pathologist generally remains in the background. If he comes on-stage, he is usually depicted as a "heavy" or salty character. The miraculous pronouncements as to cause and time of death that the fictional pathologists promulgate never cease to astound me.

"This man died sometime between 8:30 and 8:45 P.M. last Tuesday," says the pathologist-oracle.

"Can't you fix the time more exactly than that, Doctor?" asks the D.A. or private eye, as the case may be.

"I regret that medical science can do no more," responds the pathologist apologetically.

The conversation may be made to sound a little more profound with some discussion about *"rigor mortis setting in."* The best way to estimate how long a person has been dead may in some instances be to count the number of milk bottles that have accumulated on the back stoop or to use some other collateral approach, and not the examination of the body itself. Undigested food found in the stomach is often the most valuable guide to determining the time of death. I mention this because any prospective murderer who wishes to conceal the time of death of his victim is hereby advised to wash out the stomach with a tube and introduce some entirely different food items such as caviar and oysters. This should completely baffle all the sleuths.

"What is the cause of death, Doctor?" the fictionalized pathologist is asked after he has made a cursory examination of the corpse still lying on the floor.

"I suspect she died of desoxysassafras poisoning, but of course I will have to perform a complete examination to be certain," answers the pathologist. "The poison was undoubtedly introduced into the victim's fingernail polish. Observe, if you will, that the nails have turned quite black."

Once I saw a movie scene in which the pathologist (only his back was shown) was presumably performing a post-mortem examination on a body that, as far as could be seen, was enveloped in a shroud. The pathologist's elbows moved vigorously up and down, as though he were darning a large hole in a small sock. After a few such passes, he turned to the detective and said, "This man died of kidney disease." I was so fascinated that I stayed to see the scene a second time.

At one time a few years back, crime-story fiction writers used to plague the New York City medical examiners for information. I believe that most of these inquiries have stopped, for the writers soon found out that their conventionalized world of fictional crime had wandered too far afield from the actualities.

Another source of information about pathologists is to be found in occasional magazine articles written by feature writers who specialize in medical science. In these articles the pathologist is generally glamorized as an unsung hero. Our accomplishments are made to sound a great deal more impressive than they usually are, and sometimes they seem well-nigh incredible. Such articles can be annoying when the pathologist is pictured as an overgrown Boy Scout suffocating with virtue. However, other groups of doctors receive the same kind of treatment in such stories, and pathologists cannot claim to be the only victims.

Once Somerset Maugham, who himself studied medicine as a youth, wrote a short story about a doctor whose wife deserted him after minimal inducements from a casual acquaintance. In order to make the story seem plausible, the doctor had to appear to be unattractive. Maugham saw fit, therefore, to make him a grimy little pathologist, invariably pervaded to some extent by the odors of the dissecting room. As further evidence of his abominable character, the pathologist was exposed as a writer of long and absurd scientific articles to which no one paid any attention. For some perverse reason, I found the story very amusing. There was a tone of authenticity to it even though the doctor had been unfairly vilified.

I have always felt that an accurate account of the story of pathology and the considerable accomplishments of its practitioners deserves to be told to the general public. Other fields of medicine have received rather exhaustive attention, and we have not had our fair share. Furthermore, a new order of pathologist has arisen whose duties and functions are concerned largely with living patients. The old order, which I represent, dwindles in number and will soon be forgotten without its history having been adequately recorded. We were concerned almost exclusively with the

7

dead, and our major purpose was to uncover unknown diseases and to check up on the accuracy of the diagnoses that had been made on patients during life.

Up to now there has been little motivation for me to undertake the job of historian, since I cannot claim any special qualifications other than some thirty years of experience as a pathologist. I could only hope to tell the story in terms of my own restricted career. My experiences are not necessarily identical with those of other pathologists and my account of them is bound to be biased. And the story of pathology can hardly be unfolded without discussing its interrelationships with other medical specialties. In the autopsy room the pathologist is obviously concerned with the occasional failures of his practicing colleagues. Any searching analysis of the activities of pathologists could easily seem at times to be a destructive exposé of other doctors.

When I last investigated the matter several years ago, only about one death occurred out of every thirty patients admitted to a general hospital, and this death ratio continues to decline. It is thus only the thirtieth hospital patient who comes under the scrutiny of autopsy-performing pathologists. We have very little traffic with the practicing doctor's abundant and often impressive successes. Our inside story is bound to present a most unbalanced picture of the medical scene as a whole. This alone would make most pathologists hesitant about publicizing their own role in medicine.

Recently, however, I saw a television program that purported to reveal the candid inside story of pathology. It achieved this aim very effectively as far as the presentation of factual material was concerned, but the over-all impression it created, I think, left much to be desired. In this story, an old-fashioned, reactionary pathologist and a young, up-to-date, progressive new-comer to the field were set up as antagonists and the drama was based on conflict between the two. The youngster was endowed with all the virtues and the old man was loaded with vice. This was really carrying things a little too far. It made me quite sad and not a little irritated.

I believe the time has come for some reckless pathologist to break through the obscurity and misinformation that seem to surround our work and position and to divulge the real "inside" story. With considerable presumption, I have elected myself to fulfill this urgent need. I have no doubt that many of my fellow-pathologists will frown upon my decision and probably say scornfully, "I could have done a much better job myself." At the outset, I must make it clear that the opinions I shall express are strictly my own and, more than likely, do not coincide with those of any other pathologist. Most certainly they are not those of the medical profession as a whole.

When I first became a pathologist some thirty years ago, people to whom I had just been introduced would often ask me, "What field are you in, Doctor?" I would naïvely admit to being a pathologist. But I soon found out that this was a mistake. Either I would be classified by my questioner as a member of some special medical cult, such as chiropractic or osteopathy, or I would be subjected to an impatient inquisition about just what a pathologist is. This would involve me in all sorts of complicated explanations that seldom clarified anything or proved satisfactory to the skeptical questioner.

After a while I realized it was safer to answer such inquiries by merely saying, "I work in the laboratory." This sounded more dignified and usually removed the need for further elaboration. However, it was obvious that such a reply was sometimes received with suspicion, as though I were an impostor pretending to be a legitimate doctor and being very evasive about it when pinned down. Many people feel that a "doctor" should have an office and treat sick people. After years of thought on the subject I am not sure that they aren't right. At least this feeling would help preserve the continuing prestige of the practicing doctor of medicine. There is a tendency today in some learned quarters to regard practicing doctors as somewhat inferior to the investigators, the full-time medical-school doctors and the bigwig medical administrators. I don't buy it myself.

It should be apparent by now that the position of the pathologist as a doctor is so misunderstood that some enlightenment is in order. Even medical students sometimes used to ask me if I was ever going to become a regular doctor. In recent years there has been a flood of literature about the activities of the medical world, and many people have become surprisingly well informed on the subject. Just the other day, however, I was introduced to a lawyer at a cocktail party. He seemed very intelligent and knowledgeable, and made a few comments about doctors that confirmed this impression. Presently he asked me what kind of doctor I was, and being caught off guard, I injudiciously admitted I was a pathologist. "Oh," he replied knowingly, "that means you work on cancer." No doubt some pathologists are primarily oncologists, but most of us cover the gamut of disease, like roving centers on a football team. Pathologists and their function apparently remain as much of an enigma as ever to the public.

There are a number of reasons for our obscurity. First of all, the word "pathologist" can be deceptive. By derivation it means "a student of disease," and obviously it can thus be used correctly to designate all doctors of medicine and, in fact, anyone who studies disease processes. The word is sometimes used in this broad sense, and there is at present a trend to widen its usage. For example *American Men of Science*, which is sort of a *Who's Who* compilation of well-known persons engaged in all scientific pursuits, lists all medical men as pathologists. I find this pleasantly ironical, since included in this category are a number of celebrated clinicians who are not renowned for their esteem of pathologists of my kind. The word "pathology" has a nice sound to it, and it is widely used in many different connotations—which further confuses the issue of what pathologists are. For example, I notice that it is a favorite word among psychiatrists with whom pathologists have precious little traffic professionally.

11

We pathologists have appropriated our name and held it more or less successfully by a process of squatter's rights. In the nineteenth century, by common usage, it became the term applied to doctors who spent most of their time performing autopsies, probably because the practicing doctors of that day studied chiefly the symptoms of disease, while the dissectors in the mortuary were more directly concerned with the effects of disease on the organs and tissues of the body.

During the past several decades, the functions of the old-fashioned autopsy-performing pathologist have become greatly changed and at the same time broadened and diversified. This, I believe, is what led inevitably to the conflict between the two types of pathologists in the television show that precipitated me into this writing business. It was obvious that the producers of this extravaganza had little idea of the real background of the story they were projecting. In fact, I am sometimes amazed by how obscure the origins of this medical specialty seem to be even to many members of the medical profession. In any case, the diversity of the functions of present-day pathologists makes this specialty seem even more confusing to the public. People who know that some pathologists perform autopsies are very much surprised to learn that others run private laboratories or are concerned chiefly with the performance of laboratory tests. One of the purposes of this book is to explain how the science of pathology has evolved from the days of its inception, so that we pathologists can at least be more comfortable at cocktail parties.

Oversensitive persons perhaps do not care to hear much about autopsies, and doctors in general and pathologists in particular have always preferred to be reticent about them except on the occasions when they solicit consent for such examinations from the relatives of deceased patients. Then they sometimes discover that because of the distorted and inadequate information that many people have about autopsies, they have a great deal of explaining to do at a time when bereaved relatives are likely to be least receptive. The fact that autopsies are not considered a polite topic of conversation is perhaps the major reason for the ignorance of the general public about the work of pathologists. In a certain sense, pathologists are remote lineal descendants of the doctors who centuries ago robbed graves in order to carry out post-mortem dissections. It is possible that a bit of the odium attached to such ancient practices has by tradition carried over to the present-day performers of autopsies, even though there are strict laws regulating these matters and every pathologist whom I have ever met abides by these rules most scrupulously.

It is understandable that all of us should have great reverence for our relatives who have died, but much, if not all, of the objection to the performance of autopsies is based on ignorance and superstition. It is my belief that most reasonable and intelligent people have lost much of their feeling of repugnance about autopsies and no longer consider them to be an unwarranted mutilation of the dead. My belief is based on the fact that autopsy-percentage rates have risen perceptibly in almost all hospitals throughout the country and that doctors no longer find it nearly so difficult as it used to be to persuade relatives to grant consent for such examinations.

In many cases consent is given without lengthy explanations. Sometimes an agreement is reached by telephone or even simply in response to brief telegrams. Quite often a nonmedical official in the administrative office of the hospital can obtain consent without calling the doctor into the discussion. Of course there is a sizable body of unreasonable and uncooperative people who will always refuse consent for such examinations, as they sometimes do for many other medical procedures.

There is another unexpected, and still small-scale, reaction on the part of the public that makes me feel it has a latent curiosity about autopsies. This curiosity, if nurtured, could become a formidable force, insuring the continuance of this time-honored medical procedure even if the average doctor's interest in autopsies should wane, as it already shows some signs of doing in the younger generation. An enlightened public interest might also improve the morale of the pathologist and lead him to perform these examinations with the same zeal he brought to them when he hoped each case might provide important new medical discoveries. The new reaction I mentioned is reflected in the fact that the family of a patient who has died will nowadays occasionally not only grant consent for the autopsy without persuasion but insist that the findings be made known to them. In other words, an increasing number of people want accurate information as to just how their relatives died. Thirty years ago such requests were almost unheard of.

The arguments that doctors still use when necessary to obtain autopsy permission have lost most of their cogency and in some instances are even mildly specious. An appeal to the humanitarian feelings of the relatives and the claim that this particular autopsy is important to advance medical knowledge are frequently exaggerations. In any case, the implication is made and accepted that the relative is doing the doctor a favor in granting permission. If the truth were known, the relative is doing himself and his neighbors a favor, and in fact is getting a complicated and time-consuming procedure performed for nothing. In a rational and well-informed world, a prosperous family should be willing to pay for this service.

Doctors privately know this to be true. Whenever I have had occasion to perform an autopsy on the relative of a doctor (and I have never heard of a doctor who did not want one done), he has almost invariably tried very insistently to pay me for it. He knows that I have done him a tangible service. The public ought to feel the same way. If the patient's doctor were forthright about his reasons for desiring a post-mortem examination, he would say to the family, "We would like to have it done because we want to be certain that our diagnosis was correct, that we did not miss anything important, that our treatment was proper and effective, and that we did not fail to do anything that might have saved his life." As matters now stand, he cannot very well put it this way, because the relative might unjustifiably get the idea that some error had been committed.

I can speak with authority based on years of direct experience when I say that the standards of medical care are remarkably high today. I know, because I have watched them improve amazingly over the past thirty years. I firmly believe that autopsy findings have helped bring about this improvement and can continue to do so in the future, even if not many more great discoveries are likely to be made in the autopsy room. But as medical knowledge expands, other aspects of medicine compete increasingly with pathology and have the added attraction of being new. The clinician unfortunately finds he has less opportunity and inclination to visit the autopsy room, but the doctors of my own generation still frequent the place as a matter of ingrained habit. It was too much a part of their training for them to change their ways. But younger doctors may merely telephone to learn the results, and some are frank enough to indicate that all they want to know is "how to fill out the death certificate" or "what to tell the relatives." A goodly and increasing number of them make no inquiries at all about the the autopsy results except in a few especially interesting cases.

I think this is a bad trend, but of course I am hopelessly prejudiced in the matter. There are very few ways in which the quality of medical care can be accurately evaluated. Statistics showing how frequently the hospital laundry chutes are tested for sterility, or whether a unit record system is enforced, or whether the doctors meet often enough in various conferences are very fine—but they don't tell exactly what has happened to the patients. Autopsies provide a limited and selected but nevertheless very direct measure of the kind of care that is provided, as I hope to show. If the practicing doctor ceases to pay serious attention to autopsy findings, they might as well not be done at all.

In a sensible society, the family would take it for granted that an autopsy would be performed in case of death, and if they were financially able, they would be expected to pay for it. Hospital-insurance benefits, in my opinion, ought to cover the cost of autopsies just as much as they do other expenses. Such an arrangement would make it clear that performance of autopsies is both respectable and necessary. After the autopsy, the pathologist, if requested, ought to consider it his duty to talk in person to the relatives and give them as detailed an account of what he found as they are able to understand. It is my belief that if this were made possible, people would soon come to be less reluctant about granting autopsy consent. The fact that the pathologist remains an obscure figure out of public view gives his post-mortem examinations a forbidding air of mystery.

This proposal of mine may sound innocent enough, but I'm afraid that to doctors it will sound like a bombshell. In present hospital practice, if any relative asks to see the pathologist, he will rapidly discover that he is just about as available as the Dalai Lama. The hospital administrator would fear that medicolegal problems might occasionally arise; the doctor who treated the patient would be afraid that the pathologist might inadvertently say something that would reflect unfavorably upon him; and the pathologist would protest loudest of all because it would make him assume a responsibility that he would much prefer to avoid.

My impractical and impromptu suggestion will probably have no effect. A precious pathologist-patient relationship will perhaps never be developed. But if it is, I think its effects would eventually be beneficial all around. Relatives who give consent for an autopsy would get a more tangible return for it than at present. The doctors who treated the patient would show a greatly revived interest in what the autopsy reveals and would want to know what the pathologist intends to say to the family and why. Most important, the pathologist would, in my opinion, soon lose that feeling of loneliness and futility that he sometimes gets nowadays as he performs autopsies, and he would be inspired to do them in the old-fashioned meticulous way. He would also come to regard the deceased patient he examines in a more personal and less detached way than he sometimes does at present. I must confess with regret that there have been times when I have said to myself as I toiled in solitude in the autopsy room, "Why am I going through this complicated procedure when no one seems to care what I find?"

I do not mean to imply that the pathologist, if he talked to the relatives after an autopsy, would say things that would embarrass the doctors who treated the patient. He would indeed often be in a position to praise them lavishly and convincingly. It would be in poor taste for the doctors to praise themselves in this fashion. At the same time, the pathologist would acquire status as a doctor, and we are status seekers just like everyone else.

Many doctors may feel that I have just offered an oblique but nonetheless outrageous criticism of the medical profession, and I must confess that I feel a little like Galileo defying the authority of the Church. Caduceus defiled is a dangerous serpent. I can almost hear a hissing noise at the back of my neck. The medical profession has its share of anti-Voltairians who say, "I agree with everything you say, but will deny to the death your right to say it." More tersely, others simply say, "What good will it do for the public to be told these things?" I reply that medicine is a science, or ought to be one, and that science should have no secrets.

Pathologists have been referred to in the press as the doctor's doctors. At first glance this may seem like an enormous compliment, like referring to an artist's artist or a ballplayer's ballplayer to designate someone highly esteemed in his own field. I regret to say that "doctor's doctor" is not ordinarily used in this sense at all. It is used more like the phrase "a gentleman's gentleman." Clinicians and surgeons perform a service for sick people, and pathologists do the same, but only through the medium of another doctor. Some doctors get the feeling that pathologists perform services for them personally, and like to refer to the pathology department as a "service department." This point of view can easily lead to a situation in which the pathologist himself is regarded as a sort of medical servant and is treated accordingly. When the doctors of the clinical services or of the administration of a hospital start bandying the words "service department" around when they criticize the laboratory, it is time for the pathologist to start looking for another job.

Thus there are some hospitals that never seem to be able to hold a pathologist for any length of time, even though they pay him well. Sometimes I receive calls from the managers of such institutions asking if I know of any young pathologist who is looking for a job. The manager will sometimes say that the last incumbent was a very fine fellow and no one can understand why he left. He sounds then like a housewife who complains about the ungrateful and insubordinate attitude of housemaids and domestics these days.

Whenever a doctor writes a scientific article, which with considerable affectation he calls a "paper," he generally ends with a summary. Most of my writing has been of this nature, and I feel some compulsion to end this chapter in such a fashion. Instead, I will merely summarize my motives or, if you prefer, my excuses for writing this book. I want first of all to convince the public that autopsies are decent and respectable, and I want to discuss, with honesty, the reasons why they are necessary. I intend to correct any misconceptions the public may have acquired about us and show that we are not macabre or ghoulish creatures but reputable doctors. I intend also to describe the important role that pathology has played in the development of modern medicine. But, most of all, I want to say to anyone who asks me what pathologists do, "Buy my book and find out."

2

The Circuitous Road to the
Deadhouse

AFTER the television portrayal of life among pathologists was presented, I discussed the program with my younger associates and found that it had not had the same unpleasant impact on them as it had had on me. A little self-analysis made me realize that the reason for this was that I had identified myself, in a way that none of the younger men could appreciate, with the unsympathetic old pathologist who was about to be forced out of his job. To me the old pathologist's point of view had not been adequately presented, and his contribution to the hospital in the past had been shamefully downgraded.

I saw the has-been pathologist as an "academic-minded" member of the old school of pathologists who are proud and jealous of their skill with the microscope. The youngster who eventually replaced him represented to me the new "commercial-minded" pathologists who are primarily laboratory managers and to whom skill with the microscope is a minor consideration. Some acknowledgment of this was made in the television story when the young doctor failed to recognize the nature of a bone tumor and even had the nerve to argue the point with the older man, who later proved to be correct. Apparently this was not considered to be an error sufficiently grave to raise doubts about the young man's competence. (The new generation would say "competence as a *tissue* pathologist," an expression I abhor because it indicates that the study of tissues under the microscope is only a minor function of pathology.)

The youngster was a wizard at determining blood types, whereas the oldster was hopelessly behind the times on this score. The fact of the matter is that you can hire trained technicians who know as much about blood groups as any average pathologist, but you can't hire one who can tell the difference between a malignant and a benign tumor. This is something the pathologist himself has to do. The conscientious young pathologist who realizes his own deficiencies in recognizing pathological changes in tissue frequently finds it necessary to send his sections to some old "obsolete" tissue diagnostician for advice. In fact, there are certain well-known pathologists who are constantly plagued by requests for help from these presumably proficient youngsters, who frequently command much larger salaries than the men whose assistance they solicit.

When I entered the field of pathology, the senior pathologists were mainly of the old school, the one typified more or less by the villain of the television piece, and I am afraid I grew up to cherish and emulate such men. Gradually our breed of pathologist has dwindled. Unless we are protected, like the whooping crane and the buffalo, we are likely to become extinct. We have been largely displaced from the inner circles of medical schools and are not wanted in the voluntary or private hospitals. Yet I am convinced that our contribution to modern medicine has been as great as anyone's, even though we have never received adequate popular recognition. As I have indicated, it is one of the major purposes of this book to define that contribution and show its importance.

The unflattering television image of my alter ego set me to thinking just how I had managed to get myself into such a predicament, to become so unenviable a figure. How does it happen that a young man sets out hopefully to become a doctor treating patients, and ends up a doctor reading slides, a pathologist? I am a firm believer in the idea that trivial incidents and chance remarks help shape destiny, although the underlying temperament and personality of each person no doubt play a dominant role in his own fate. I suspect I became a pathologist partly by intention, partly as an escape from the alternatives, but largely through happenstance.

I should like to pretend that I was a wizard as a medical student, but I am afraid there are still too many of my classmates about who may remember me and know better. In truth, I was a much-befuddled student, strangely shy and quite tongue-tied. When I did venture a remark in class, it unfortunately came forth most often in the form of a misguided wisecrack that did not endear me to the faculty members.

During my first year as a medical student I became enslaved by an unfortunate addiction. It was my habit to lunch on a liverwurst sandwich and three bottles of etherized beer, which I had at a speakeasy located near the medical school. I would return to my afternoon classes in a slightly anesthetized condition and take a seat in the last row of the precipitous amphitheater that served as a lecture room. I believed that in this unobtrusive position I was relatively protected against becoming involved in any impromptu quizzing. The lecturer in this post-luncheon class was a most distinguished gentleman and probably a very talented teacher. I never really found out. He had a bald and very glistening pate, and the lights just above him produced fascinating reflections. My etherized attention would become focused on these reflections and I would promptly go into a sort of hypnotic or narcoleptic trance from which I would recover only when the class was over.

Consequently, when my more sporting fellow-students compiled, for betting-pool purposes, lists of students least likely to succeed to the second year, my name figured prominently. They miscalculated, chiefly because they were unaware of the fact that I possessed a pretty little talent for making sweeping generalizations and odious comparisons, which stood me in good stead on the kind of long-answer written examinations in vogue at the time. This book, I believe, will substantiate my claim to these talents.

In the vacation period after the first year's work, I spent the summer reading MacCallum's *A Textbook of Pathology*, hoping to get a head start for the second-year studies. It turned out to be fascinating reading for me. In fact, it is the only textbook that I have ever read with pleasure, and I have no doubt that it first kindled in me an impulse to become a pathologist. Later the professor of pathology, who also served as dean of the medical school, proved to be one of the most extraordinarily dynamic personalities I have ever encountered. His lectures were dramatic and he made pathology sound like a most exciting and vital science. This further awakened a desire on my part to go into this specialty. I was not alone among the students in this feeling. Quite a few of my classmates accepted appointments in pathology after they were graduated, and four of us, to my knowledge, have remained in this field. I am pleased to report that at least the other three have had distinguished careers. I have subsequently discovered that most medical schools have on their faculties one or more fascinating personalities who exercise great influence on the ambitions and subsequent careers of the students. These shining, magnetic figures can appear in almost any department of the school.

During the second-year course, I changed from liverwurst and beer to bologna sandwiches for lunch and did much better, although I continued in my reckless career of alienating the affections of important faculty dignitaries with innocently intended remarks that somehow turned out to seem insolent. For example, when the associate professor of pathology who was in charge of teaching asked me how I would tell by examining a body after death whether or not the person had been lame during life, I was unable to supply the proper answer. He persisted in badgering me about it until, finally, I blurted out that I would look in the armpits for calluses caused by the use of crutches. This remark met with stony silence, and I could see the professor mentally marking up a black score against my name as a no-good Joe.

This particular teacher, and I confess he was an excellent one, had the habit of tramping back and forth on the podium in a very rhythmic way throughout his entire lecture. I became curious about the distance that he covered. Since he consistently took eight steps forward, then turned and retraced his steps at a rate of about ten complete trips per minute, it was simple to calculate that he tramped three miles during an hour lecture. One day while entering this class I said to a fellow classmate, "Let's go watch Dr. X take his three-mile constitutional." My classmate repeated this remark to the professor, and if the latter ever had any doubts about my reprehensibility, this incident completely removed them. Any student who spent the entire lecture hour (as he assumed) counting his steps instead of listening to his pearls of wisdom was obviously an undesirable character. It soon became apparent that I could hardly hope for an appointment in that pathology department.

At the first clinic held at the beginning of my third year, I offended again. The professor of medicine uncovered the abdomen of a patient who had been wheeled into the amphitheater. He beckoned to me. I was, as usual, perched far up in the back row. "Would you mind coming down here and telling us what you can see?" he asked. "Rose spots," I answered, without so much as budging from my seat. The professor glared at me and went on with the case presentation. I don't believe he ever spoke to me again during my remaining two years as a student, much to my dismay.

Perhaps I should explain the nature of my *faux pas*. Rose spots are a very faint rash sometimes found on the abdomens of patients with typhoid fever. To see them at a lecture you usually had to be quite close to the patient. It was obvious that I couldn't see them from my position. I was only proceeding on the premise that the first patient presented at the first clinic of the year was bound to be a typhoid patient, and why else would the abdomen be exposed as a starter?

The circumstances that made my speculations reasonable were that at this time (circa 1928) there were still a few patients with typhoid fever in the wards of hospitals, but usually only during the late summer or early fall. The faculty reasoned that if they didn't show the students a case of typhoid at that time, they might never have another opportunity. If memory serves me, I believe that the first chapter in Osler's memorable and classic textbook of medicine is devoted to typhoid fever for this reason. What I failed to take into account was that by being a smart aleck about it I was accusing the professor of stereotyped, perennially repetitive teaching methods, a personal insult he was not likely to overlook. In any case, thereafter I could discount my chances of obtaining an internship on his service.

In this particular medical school every student was required to do some original piece of work and write a thesis before graduation. When I tell present-day students about this, they don't quite believe me, for they are convinced that student participation in research was not invented until after the Second World War. In order to fulfill this requirement, we had to be accepted officially by some department of the school in which the work was to be carried out. As I became *persona non grata* in more and more departments, I began to despair of ever finding a suitable niche for myself. One day, in my third year, one of the professors of pediatrics took a group of us students on "rounds" in the isolation building of the hospital. He stopped at the door of a room in which we could see a youngster in bed who had a tightly fitting single goggle on his right eye. The doctor stopped us at the threshold. "Which eye is infected?" he asked. "Left eye," I said very quickly, before someone else beat me to it. The professor seemed pleased, and I knew that I had at last found a home in which to do my thesis. The goggle was obviously on the right eye to keep it from becoming infected. Of such incidents are the careers of men fashioned.

My new mentor, although listed officially as a pediatrician, was really a brilliant antigen-antibody boy in the best von Behring and Kitasato tradition. Lest it be thought that I say this disparagingly, I hasten to add that I became more devoted to this man than I have been to anyone else I ever met in medicine. In fact, I keep his photograph in the top drawer of my desk to this day and would hang it on the wall if I didn't think this practice pretty sticky. It's just a matter of personal preference. Such mementos always make me think of the stuffed moose heads and mounted game fish one sees on the walls of hunting lodges.

In my fourth year I was enormously flattered when the same faculty adviser urged me to stay on as an intern in pediatrics. I confessed rather ashamedly that squalling brats who could not even tell you where their pains were did not move me to as much compassion as they should have. "What difference does that make?" said my adviser. "They have as interesting diseases as anyone else, don't they?" His own interests were chiefly in the nature of infectious diseases, and that is how he happened to become a pediatrician, since children are vulnerable to a greater variety of infections than adults. If I had been completely truthful, I would have confessed that I felt intellectually too inferior to cope with the anfractuous antics of capriciously amplectant antigens and antibodies. Instead, I divulged my intention of becoming a pathologist. He looked at me as a banker might at a son who had just announced that he intends to join the Communist Party. But a couple of weeks later he came into the cubbyhole in which I labored, and announced very curtly that he had obtained an appointment for me as an intern in pathology in a well-known New York hospital.

It seems that my patron, who was an ardent dry-fly fisherman, had met the pathologist who was to be my future boss on a fishing trip and amid a discussion of the relative merits of a royal coachman and a Doberman pinscher, my future had been decided. It's a strange world in which a bit of colored feather tied to a fish hook can set the pattern of a man's life. Yes, I know, it's a dog.

The pediatrics professor never again discussed the matter with me, but shortly before I was graduated, someone inquired of him in my presence whether I planned to continue the work I was doing for my thesis during the following year. "Haven't you heard?" replied the pediatrician. "He is going to New York to learn how to 'read' slides." It was the only unkind thing he ever said to me.

3

A Career as a Pathologist

MY PENCHANT for maladroit behavior continued to haunt me as I went about the business of learning how to be a pathologist. One day shortly after I began my internship, a doctor with whom I was unfamiliar wandered into the autopsy room. I mistook him for one of the clinicians who had come to learn about the findings in the case in which I was performing an autopsy. I proceeded to demonstrate the "lesions" in a somewhat condescending, if not patronizing, manner. The word "lesion" is a term that pathologists apply to all manner of tissue damage, whether it be a cancer, an abscess or even a mere hemorrhage. A mosquito bite is a lesion too.

My visitor let me ramble on, maintaining a rather charged and, as it seems to me in retrospect, a slightly cruel silence. He did not identify himself, but very shortly thereafter I learned that he was the famed prima donna of the pathology staff, who had just returned from a sabbatical leave abroad. It took me quite a while to overcome most of the bad effects of this inauspicious introduction. For several years to come, this important member of the staff regarded me with a slight disdain. He was, however, a man who showed a great deal of kindness and understanding to his underlings, especially if they were in any kind of trouble, and since I was frequently in predicaments, he eventually forgave my initial brash behavior. At least to a degree.

In that bygone period, learning to become a competent pathologist consisted largely of learning how to perform autopsies proficiently and how to interpret the results in such a way as to disclose the underlying nature of the patient's illness, trace how it had developed and spread, demonstrate its causes (if it was possible to show them) and determine the events that immediately preceded the demise and made it inevitable. Technically such an evaluation is called a study of the "pathogenesis" of disease. Changes in tissues or organs that are so distinctive that they reveal the nature of a disease process are called "pathognomonic." Clinicians in those days were interested in and wanted to learn about all these phases of their patients' illnesses. Nowadays there is a disturbing tendency among many clinicians to limit their interests chiefly to the immediate causes of death. To me this seems a superficial attitude. To the old-fashioned pathologist, the terminal events in a patient's fatal illness are only incidental episodes, made more or less inevitable and unavoidable by the underlying disease, which may have been developing for a long time. The pathologist considers this underlying disease to be the real cause of death.

Every aspiring young pathologist is likely to regard his own superior as the greatest pathologist of all time, at least during the initial stages of his training. This, I think, is understandable. The chief knows so much, while you know so little, that he seems to be a veritable fount of knowledge. You may have pondered, without getting anywhere, over the meaning of some peculiar alteration in tissue as seen under the microscope, and he, very casually and effortlessly, gives you the answer that at once makes everything obvious. Later on, when you acquire a superficial smattering of pathological knowledge, you are apt to change your attitude and become hypercritical of your chief's cautiousness and conservatism.

I think I had better reason than most young trainees for idolizing and revering my teachers. They had learned their pathology at the feet of the masters in Baltimore and New York, and I, in effect, was learning mine in a similar position. In moments of depression nowadays, I sometimes strongly suspect that the old pathologist who had let me make a fool of myself in the autopsy room on that early day in my career had forgotten more pathology than I will ever know.

34

Until I entered the autopsy room as a first-year medical student I had never seen a dead body. It might be suspected that dealing with the dead could be repugnant, and difficult to become accustomed to. This was never any great problem to me, or in fact to most of the other young pathologists I have known. I do not deny that the kind of work that we do may affect our point of view and attitude. Many of us develop a certain type of cynicism that may be disturbing to the average layman. It is hard to take human life very seriously if you deal too exclusively with the dead, and it is also sometimes difficult to believe in the dignity of man after you have handled the innards of countless bodies. Working pathologists are seldom stuffy or pompous. We are more likely to be sardonic and realistic in an undignified sort of way. I mention this because I strongly suspect that the flavor of such an attitude may be all too obvious in this book.

During the first few months of my internship, I experienced unpleasant recurring nightmares in which I dreamed I was performing autopsies on myself. I suppose psychiatrists could make much of this. I attributed my dreams to the poor quality of hospital food and to my own bad habit of indulging in the midnight meal that was available every night. But the nightmares nevertheless became very troublesome. Late one night I was awakened from such a dream and asked to perform a rush autopsy on a young girl who had just died of rheumatic heart disease and whose body had to be sent by train to her home town for burial. In ordinary circumstances, the bodies of those who die in the wards are first sent to the mortuary refrigerators, but in this case, because of the need for speed, it was sent directly to the autopsy room.

I was disturbed by the fact that the body was still warm and looked very lifelike indeed. With some effort of will, I proceeded with my gruesome chore. And when I exposed the heart and touched it, it began to twitch vigorously and in rhythm. It wasn't exactly a forceful heartbeat, but it was enough to make me break out in a cold sweat. The examination had already gone too far even to consider possible resuscitation. I was distinctly unhappy about the state of affairs. Presently the heart stopped its agitation, and I recovered from my confusion. To this day, I secretly consider myself a pioneer in the art of cardiac massaging, a distinction I do not particularly cherish since I have a poor regard for cardiac masseurs in general. I see their many inevitable failures, not those dramatic successes you read about in the papers.

This unpleasant incident had a fortunate aftermath. Thereafter I ceased dreaming about carving up myself on an autopsy table. On the few occasions when this type of dream intruded, I was usually performing an autopsy on someone I didn't particularly like. This altered dream, while still discomforting, was not without its recompense.

A technically skillful pathologist can perform a complete autopsy in about an hour and a half without making any special effort to speed things up. A clumsy beginner may take four hours or longer. During the procedure, we examine and describe all the major organs of the body and take small samples that will later be processed and made into very thin stained films of tissue and mounted on glass slides for examination under the microscope. The initial study made during the autopsy is called the gross description. After he has completed both the gross and microscopic examinations, the pathologist writes a summary that attempts to relate the findings to one another and to the clinical events that preceded the death of the patient. Thus he sets down a complete story of the illness. He also compiles a list of diagnoses or, in other words, gives names to the abnormalities found. Such a complete study takes time, usually from four to eight weeks in a well-organized service.

Before a pathologist begins an autopsy, he must check to see that the consent slip has been signed by the nearest of kin, properly witnessed and approved by a designated administrative official of the hospital. If there is evidence that the case has any medicolegal aspect—if, for instance, death resulted from an automobile accident or an assault—the case is promptly referred to and its disposition decided by the medical examiner's office. If everything is in order, however, the pathologist reads the clinical history of the patient before he begins his examination. Better still, if the doctors who treated the patient are available, he discusses with them the problems involved. This preliminary orientation is most essential, for it helps the pathologist decide what he must look for. Sometimes the nature of the major disease processes involved is evident at the time the autopsy is performed. Not too infrequently, their nature becomes apparent only after the pathologist has had a chance to examine the microscopic sections. Sometimes he finds that the impressions formed at the time of autopsy are completely wrong or that normal-looking organs are in fact badly diseased.

It would be misleading to pretend that the pathologist can always tell exactly why a patient has died or exactly what ailed the patient. Sometimes we can provide only partial or speculative answers. Occasionally we are just as baffled after a complete workup as we were when we started. If a thorough examination has been performed, there will very likely be findings for which we have no explanation at all. I have done autopsies on very old ladies and found nothing abnormal other than the generalized wasting away that accompanies old age. These rare instances make me think at times that perhaps Metchnikoff was right— that there really is something equivalent to physiological, or natural, death in man, and that scientists who talk of prolonging life much beyond a hundred years have their work cut out for them. Most of the time we do find very definite abnormalities. And when we don't, we are forced to construct the best diagnosis we can make.

When I was a trainee, most pathology departments

I knew about held weekly or even biweekly autopsy slide-review conferences. All the members of the staff, with their microscopes, would congregate in a conference room, where detailed findings of each autopsy were presented in their entirety to the presiding chief. Doubtful issues were discussed or argued about. At the conclusion of each presentation, the chief would dictate to the junior member who had performed the autopsy what we called the "final note." My particular chief had a special genius for dictating very learned and informative summaries of this type. I never ceased to marvel at the way he could make seemingly unrelated and sometimes insignificant data fit together and form a logical chain of events that laid bare the essential nature of the patient's disease. I might be at a complete loss as to how to interpret what I had found and he, in a few sentences, could make everything clear.

Autopsies became for me a fascinating pursuit, much more challenging and provocative than any other I have known. After thirty years I have never lost my zest for trying to interpret autopsy findings. No two people ever die in exactly the same way, nor are the same disease processes in different persons ever identical. There is a kind of retribution in the fact that people who have led dull and drab lives may, before they inherit their six feet of earth, die of the most exciting and exotic diseases and perhaps even be immortalized on the pages of a medical publication. On the other hand, I think it very fitting that the most glamorous and fortunate people frequently die of commonplace illnesses.

Whatever I know about the pathology of human disease I learned more in these group conferences than in the autopsy room. Nevertheless, these conferences were tedious, tiring and time-consuming. Many of us rebelled against them the way prizefighters rebel against training-camp tedium or student musicians against practicing scales for hours on end. To become skillful in most specialized kinds of work usually requires arduous, prolonged and repetitious practice in certain of its elementary but key phases. Our pathological conferences would start at 9 A.M. and continue uninterruptedly to about 1 P.M. During this time we would review four or five autopsies and examine perhaps a hundred and fifty slides. We would emerge bleary-eyed and exhausted. But that is the way to become a pathologist. Any short cuts are strictly dead ends.

Conferences of this type have gradually been abandoned in many pathology departments, or they have been greatly abridged or curtailed. Many of the present-day senior pathologists consider them too time-consuming, and our current crop of pampered residents would not stand for them. Today, senior members frequently check autopsy findings individually with the residents, and the whole process may take no more than ten or fifteen minutes for each case. Pathologists nowadays have acquired many other functions, and the autopsy-case load is a burden to be liquidated as simply as possible. I still prefer the old method. To me, a superficially worked-up autopsy might just as well not have been done at all.

As a young trainee, I also taught second-year medical students by demonstrating specimens to them in the autopsy room or helping them in the classroom with their sets of slides on pathological processes. I taught with zest if not with skill. In general, teaching was fun, but I would be untruthful if I did not admit that it was sometimes boring. Teaching small groups of students was far more rewarding than lecturing to large groups. The students' attitudes also determine whether or not teaching is a burden or a pleasure. The student body of any one class as a whole, for some inexplicable reason, develops a distinctive personality of its own. "Good" classes seem to alternate with "poor" ones, so that I, in effect, enjoyed teaching every other year and disliked it in the intervening ones.

Young instructors tend to be intolerant, harsh and tyrannical, and I am sure some of my former students who may remember me from my early teaching days do so with no great affection. After I had been at it a number of years, I managed to hurt grievously the feelings of one relatively innocuous student. Every medical faculty has one or more father-confessors to whom students bring their troubles. I was never one of these. In this instance, the aggrieved student brought his complaint about me to the much-esteemed leading father-confessor of the school. The latter dressed me down in a way I shall never forget, and thereafter I was never deliberately unkind to any other student, however great the provocation. Nowadays I save my ammunition for residents.

Lecturing to the entire second-year class of medical students was also one of my duties, and I cannot say that I excelled at it. About the only really great oratorical achievement of my career occurred at a late stage when I was invited to address the Medical Society of Costa Rica while there with a delegation of American doctors that had been sent to learn about tropical diseases. It was believed at the time that soldiers returning from the far parts of the earth at the close of World War II might bring back a variety of strange diseases. This belief proved largely groundless, but at the time it seemed wise to send groups of doctors to Central America to learn about these diseases in order to be prepared for such an eventuality. I was among one of the last groups to be sent.

At the end of my lecture, whose subject I cannot even remember, the audience stood up as one man and gave me a resounding ovation. The only drawback was that not one of them understood a word of English. The reason for my outstanding success was that I gesticulate very nicely when I talk, open-end style.

If my visit to Costa Rica did much to restore my self-esteem as an orator, it had the opposite effect on my conceit as an accomplished autopsy prosector. I had long cherished the belief that my technique in the autopsy room was unsurpassable. In the hospital at Costa Rica, there were three autopsy-room assistants, known as dieners, who were named, respectively, Raffaillo, Umberto and Ridolfo. Raffaillo was the leader, and the most accomplished technical virtuoso I have ever seen in any autopsy room. He had never worn a pair of shoes in his life, nor ever had a legitimate barbershop type of haircut, but his dissecting technique was impeccable. Furthermore, he was a superb mimic. Each delegation of visiting American doctors had one pathologist. Raffaillo watched each of these perform and could imitate any one of them to perfection. You could say to him, "Do an autopsy like Dr. X of Chicago or Dr. Y of Boston," and Raffaillo would graciously oblige. Dressed in a surgeon's scrub-suit with cap and mask, and barefoot, he was a sight to behold. At the same time, I found it somewhat humiliating to think that the best autopsy-performing pathologist I ever saw should have been so flagrantly unshod.

My third pursuit as an aspiring young pathologist was to carry out original investigations. I planned a great many research projects, actually started a fair number, but—I regret to say—brought only a few to fruition. The medical woods are full of thwarted and frustrated would-be researchers. Almost every doctor would like to undertake original investigations. Most of them just dream or talk about it. Some of us (and I include myself in this group) never cease trying, but lack the required native talent and are not very productive.

Real research men are born, not made. They do not need encouragement to perform experiments, nor can they be discouraged—either by lack of money or equipment, by nagging wives or the needs of their children. The present drive to encourage young students to plan careers in research is to me a little absurd. You couldn't keep the potentially productive ones out if you tried. What is likely to happen is that many young men may be induced to lead lives of quiet frustration attempting to perform something for which they are not qualified.

Every once in a while natural researchers will unexpectedly turn up on my resident staff. I admire such characters enormously and give great leeway to them, but I know that they will be a pain in the neck about carrying on their routine resident duties. The other residents generally have to do their work for them and often complain that they, too, want to do experimental work. But the ordinary resident never gets much beyond the talking stage.

It is difficult to analyze the temperaments (and there are more than one) that make certain persons natural investigators. Ability and relentless drive they must certainly have, but most of all they need boundless enthusiasm that gives substance to their dreams. Never for a moment must they question the potential importance of the work they are doing. It is this capacity I lack, if not others. When I go to a scientific meeting, I am depressed by what seems to me to be the picayune character of the work so many other investigators report, and my own small efforts suddenly seem equally negligible. The true researcher comes away from such meetings greatly stimulated.

However, I am frank to admit that I harbor nothing but purified malice and triple-distilled envy for all successful researchers. Success in this field is the thing, above all others, I would have liked to achieve. I say this because in the ensuing pages I am apt to throw some below-the-belt punches at the researchers. It is just as well that I confess the genesis of this attitude at the start. Even without prizes and awards, the successful investigator gets more than his fair share of the good things in life. If you have ever seen a researcher at the moment when a significant experiment has come through for him, you would realize that all encomiums from outsiders are to a certain extent superfluous. The researcher can afford indifference to my criticism and doesn't need my praise. I paraphrase a witty commentator: at the moment of successful impregnation, does the sperm require a testimonial from the ovum?

Early in my career, when I was first in the process of realizing my shortcomings as an original investigator, a biography of the Russian scientist Pavlov appeared. In it he was quoted as having spoken contemptuously of the vast majority of researchers and of having compared them to circus riders, who prance about on the broad backs of Percherons as they circle round and round the ring and never get anywhere. Pavlov was a great man, and it is permissible for the great to make sweeping generalizations. All the same, I think he was a little unfair. There is room for all kinds of investigators—the scavengers who merely clean up the crumbs left by other people's discoveries, the "me too" group who simply repeat with minor modifications the work of others, and the well-kept drug-house scientists who make those marvelous medications that are so expensively beneficial to us all. We are needed off-stage and in the wings, if not in the spotlight. If nothing else, we provide an audience for the talented researchers.

Nevertheless, I am glad that routine pathology has made it possible for me to get off the back of the Percheron a good part of the time. Nowadays I perform drab little planned experiments that won't make much difference, whether they come out positive or not. Secretly I have always taken absurd and irrational little flyers in experiments that I would not dream of telling anyone about. To do so would expose me to ridicule. I do this in the spirit of a man who buys tickets in the sweepstakes. I know full well that carelessly planned and superficial quickie experiments never pan out, but it's nice to dream of drawing a horse, although you know you never will.

During the past thirty years I have performed, supervised or checked out more than fifteen thousand autopsies, examined more than sixty thousand surgical specimens, not counting hernial sacs and varicose veins, and taught upward of three thousand medical students, not counting the ones who flunked out. Somewhere along the line you might suspect that I should have become an accomplished pathologist, but I still feel like a rank beginner. The reason for this is that each week I still see, through the magic microscope or in the autopsy room, as many new things, as much with which I am unfamiliar, as when I first started out. This is one of the rewards of being a pathologist. The work never grows stale. Fame, fortune and the accolades of any particular multitude will never be mine, but I have enjoyed my work, which is perhaps an even better compensation. What promotions and meager honors have come my way have accrued largely by attrition and seniority. Once I was chosen to be an official of a local pathological society, but this was a sentimental gesture on the part of colleagues to reward me for having recovered from tuberculosis and not, I'm afraid, a tribute to my prestige as a pathologist.

Nowadays young pathologists spend four years learning their craft and only two of them are spent on autopsies or pathological tissue specimens. At the end of this time, they take an examination which, if they pass it, qualifies them as authentic members of their craft. Most of them discover that they still have a great deal to learn. But routine pathology, I repeat, has its own sweet reward. Whenever I find myself depressed by the cares of this world and life becomes *"immer schlimmer,"* as one of my radiological friends puts it, I can seek solace in the autopsy room. There I will most likely come upon some magnificent collector's-item type of lesion, bigger and more colorful than any I have ever seen before. It will be radiant-hued in all shades of the spectrum, including metanil-yellow,

47

cresyl-violet, safranine-beige, pyronine-green and scarlet-red, delicately textured and exquisitely patterned. Life suddenly becomes rich and full again, and my only regret is that I cannot congratulate the poor victim who brought forth such a masterpiece. When my mathematician and physicist friends tell me scornfully that mine is an impure science, I cheerfully say the hell with them.

4

Respectability in the Autopsy Room

IN THAT television story about pathologists the scene that most irritated and saddened me was the one in which two junior members of the staff were shown performing an autopsy in a lackadaisical manner. The observer could easily have felt that pathologists are habitually frivolous and irreverent about their work. There is nothing about an autopsy to arouse such an attitude. The atmosphere is inevitably a solemn and sober one.

The television play could not, of course, raise the question of sloppiness in autopsy technique, but that would have been a more pertinent matter. It is possible to be both solemn and sloppy at the same time. The nature of the examination can easily lead to untidiness, but responsible pathologists do not and never have tolerated sloppiness in the autopsy room. The conditions under which autopsies used to be performed were such that the pathologist was virtually compelled by the presence of a considerable audience to maintain an atmosphere of respectability even if he happened to be an untidy person by nature.

If there is any tendency toward relaxation in deportment in the autopsy room, and I regret to admit that this is so, it has been introduced by the younger generation of pathologists, who perform post-mortem examinations in a changed atmosphere, which tends to encourage such behavior. The public hears about the nature of autopsy procedures only at second hand. Exaggerated stories about callous actions in the autopsy room have helped create distorted ideas about the way these examinations are performed. It is my belief that if the public had an enlightened attitude about autopsies, any laxity on the part of pathologist that may have developed in recent years would soon vanish.

The fine young "doctor's doctor" type of neopathologist who replaced the supposedly crude old one in the television drama displayed his high standards and great delicacy by insisting that the face of the person undergoing examination be covered by a towel. In practice this is often done. It is a refinement, however, that I believe is both precious and usually unnecessary.

The face of the deceased should be covered whenever he is a personal friend of anyone present. This is to spare the feelings of the living, not of the dead. In any other circumstance it is a superfluous gesture. In fact, it suggests that something slightly shameful is taking place. Ideally, a pathologist and his assistants should conduct an autopsy in such a way that if anyone close to the person under examination were to enter unexpectedly at any time, he would not be offended by what he saw. There is no reason why the disciplined attention to standards of the operating amphitheater should not be observed in the autopsy room. I regret to say that such standards are not always maintained today and, if anything, laxity is on the upswing.

During my first autopsy I was considerably flustered by my own ineptness and by the fact that I was surrounded three deep by clinical dignitaries. (This was back in the days when clinicians wouldn't dream of missing any part of an autopsy on one of their patients.) Suddenly I heard a harsh whisper in my left ear, "You have blood on your arm!" It was my chief, who turned abruptly and left the room. I looked at the undersurface of my right forearm and there was a speck of blood about a quarter of an inch wide. My chief's reaction reflects the kind of atmosphere in which autopsies were once performed.

Such conditions still prevail in many autopsy rooms, but unhappily there are others that sometimes resemble an abattoir. Unmentionable fluids and excretions may be carelessly spattered about. The pathologist may be indifferent to unsightly spillage as he becomes absorbed in his examination. If you protest against the lack of care, the breach of old professional standards, the young pathologist may look at you incredulously, as though you were some eccentric crank, and say with an injured air, "What difference does it make?"

I am an autopsy-performing pathologist, and I believe in the need for autopsies, but I would hesitate to consent to one on myself or on any of my relatives if I thought it would be done without respect for proper practice. There are a number of reasons for this deterioration in technique. First and foremost among these is the decline in clinicians' attendance at autopsies. When we pathologists had a sizable audience, we put on our company manners and remained on our best behavior. If you work more or less in solitude, you tend to become careless and indifferent. When senior pathologists, adept at performing autopsies by reason of long experience, noticed that the audience had dwindled, they became less eager to perform them in person. Soon the very junior, inexperienced members of the staff did most of them, and the older members only checked their findings afterward. Many such beginners had never watched a dexterous and highly skilled pathologist perform an autopsy.

In the old days the senior pathologists took their regular turns in the autopsy room and, when their equivalents on the clinical staff were present, often put on a show to demonstrate not only their profound knowledge but their technical virtuosity. The junior members hung around to pick up little tricks of technique. They vied with one another to perfect their own skills and attempted to emulate their chiefs. They were taught how to hold and handle each special instrument, whether a costotome, an enterotome or a clavicle knife. The technique of procedure was rigidly set out. Each step in the autopsy was a prescribed maneuver that could be done only in one way. The whole examination was as formalized as a ballet routine. An expert autopsy pathologist in action gave an impressive show of skill.

As I have said, senior pathologists can now find more important things to do than performing autopsies before an empty house. If they have any spare time, they prefer to carry on original investigations. I can understand their feelings in the matter and am not criticizing them, but all the same it has reached the point where senior residents who have never been adequately instructed themselves now teach junior residents how to do autopsies, or the latter simply devise their own horrid routines.

Since I am an obstinate reactionary, I still, old and stiff as I am, take a turn at an autopsy now and then just to convince my residents that no pathologist should ever feel too important to perform it. Recently one of the administrative officials of my hospital was quite surprised when he learned about this. "What have you got residents for?" he inquired, as though he suspected I was slightly touched in the head.

Corruption in autopsy etiquette began in the thirties. At this time there was a sudden influx of expatriate doctors fleeing from possible internment in Hitler's concentration camps. These refugee doctors had been specialists in a wide variety of fields, but many of them had had training in pathology at some time in the past, since this is a common feature of European medical education. Many of them were very gifted doctors and some were talented pathologists. Since, when they first arrived, they could neither speak English well nor obtain licenses to practice medicine immediately, many took positions as assistants in pathology until they could get their bearings. Not a few of these came from institutions where the major portion of the autopsy had been done by laboratory assistants known as dieners, unless there were transient American doctors around willing to do them without being paid. When a diener performs the initial stages of an autopsy that is to be completed later by a pathologist, the procedure usually differs radically from the kind of autopsy a pathologist does entirely by himself.

In any case, new practices in autopsy technique, many of them short cuts, came into vogue and much of the old order rapidly passed away. I remember protesting to a refugee assistant about his strange methods. He replied, "Ah, zees is zee method at zee great Rokitansky." This stopped me. I had been trained in the tradition of William Welch, who had been trained by Cohnheim, who in turn was in the direct line of Virchovians. But Rokitansky was a formidable figure in the history of pathology. In fact, he antedated Virchow. I did a little investigating to find out what went on in the time of the great Rokitansky.

The custom of the period appeared to me to be something like this: Each day the morgue attendant or diener would eviscerate the bodies of those to be examined, in much the same way a housewife cleans a chicken. The internal organs, in one solid block, would be placed in rows on a table. Meanwhile, the pathologist and his cronies would be sitting at the local café ogling the girls and sipping slivovitz. When the time came for the pathologist to do his daily stint, he would stagger to the dissecting room, screw a bifocal monocle upside down into one bloodshot eye and then point his walking stick waveringly in the general direction of one of the eviscerations. *"Das ist ein Karcinom,"* he would proclaim, and having delivered this portentous revelation, he would wander back to the café to continue his never-ending experiment in the effects of slivovitz on internal metabolism.

Many of the refugee doctors were stimulating people and exerted great influence on the pathology residents with whom they came in contact. After a few years, having learned English and obtained their licenses, many of them went back to their original specialties, but the changes in autopsy technique that they introduced were never eradicated. Disciples of the cult of Rokitansky still carry on the brutalities of the old master, and they don't even have the decency to drink the slivovitz that might account for their debaucheries. To this day, when I upbraid a callow resident for some awful mess that he has produced in the autopsy room, he replies (knowing full well my prejudices in the matter), "Zees is zee method of zee great Rokitansky."

A third and less tangible factor has led to the coarsening of the pathologist's manners. Since the Second World War, the general public is less horrified than ever before by the idea of autopsy. When relatives refuse to sign consents today, it is most often because they are so shocked and grief-stricken by the death in the family that they can't respond rationally to any kind of request. They don't refuse consent because they consider autopsies an unwarranted mutilation. Today there is very little organized resistance to autopsies. Some funeral directors are privately opposed, chiefly from a business point of view. Autopsies sometimes cause delay in burial plans, although usually this is inconsequential. The clergy of the major religious faiths do not oppose autopsies except in isolated cases. It has been quite clearly established that autopsies do not conflict with religious beliefs or practices.

This change in attitude toward autopsies becomes another of the factors that have altered the atmosphere in which they are performed. Once we worried about whether the relatives would regret having signed the consent and complain later. We were, therefore, much more concerned about the way we performed examinations. Legal suits over autopsy examinations have now practically disappeared, and in the few cases that come to trial the damages are trivial even if illegalities were involved. In such cases jurors have lost much of their sympathy for relatives. The autopsy

pathologist enjoys a new relative immunity from mal-
practice suits, and his insurance rates have actually
fallen. I do not contend that this factor has greatly influenced autopsy technique in any direct way, but in
subtle ways it may have helped to lower the standards.

Premedical students can be divided into two main
categories in regard to their professed future aspirations. There is the daddyoblastic group, whose members
hope to become surgeons, and the mommyoblastic,
whose members dream of a full life in psychiatry. Few
consider the possibility of becoming a pathologist. They
are crushed if you even mention such a dreary fate.
When they get to medical school they become less
certain and much more reticent about their future
plans. There is not as much freedom of choice as you
might imagine as to what their ultimate fate will be.
Their choice is likely to be heavily influenced by special, unexpected opportunities that may come their
way, and to a large extent their basic personalities and
temperaments determine the field of medicine in which
they will end up.

As a prophet of the shape of things to come, I have
established a lifelong record of uninterrupted dismal
failure. It includes my statement of December 7, 1941:
"The whole thing will probably blow over in a day or
two." Nevertheless, I like to think that I can predict
what will become of medical students after they have
reached their third or fourth year. The high-strung
type I assign to psychiatry. The All-American boy I
see as a surgeon. The cryptosadist, I find, tends toward

pediatrics. I think the pretty boy has a bright future in gynecology; the rough-and-ready types in urology or orthopedics. I expect the pleasant, not-too-profound type to drift into ophthalmology or dermatology, as I find the Boy Scout a natural for the research laboratory and the average solid citizen a born general practitioner. I'm sure suave Noel Coward, Jr., is destined to slick his way into cardiology or gastroenterology. How do these predictions work out? Years later the hulking ex-professional football player comes back to visit you. What line of work did he end up in? He's a gynecologist.

And what kind of medical student went into pathology in my time? Perhaps you can guess. It was usually the negativistic cynic of the class. But this has since changed. Now it is more likely to be the gravy-train type looking for an easy berth. Of course it is barely possible that I have exaggerated just a little bit.

The point I am trying to make is that there has been a marked change in the kind of student who is attracted to pathology, and that this circumstance has also resulted in a changed attitude about the importance of fastidious techniques. Once the prospective pathologist was completely fascinated by pathology itself. He was willing to work for a pittance if only he could do pathology. He often stayed around medical schools for years, working for little more than subsistence, and he would spurn more lucrative offers from private hospital laboratories. There was once a resident in pathology at Johns Hopkins who stayed on for fifteen years. I myself remained a resident for five years and even then regretted leaving the job. Because we cherished the work, because it was important to us, we were fussy about methods and manners.

Today's prospective pathologist has a much more relaxed feeling about his work. He thinks of it as a satisfactory way of earning a pleasant living without being exposed to too much stress and strain, a job with a fair amount of security. Pathology has become a skilled trade with a strong union and plenty of openings. Delicacy in the autopsy room doesn't necessarily fit into this picture, especially if no one appreciates it.

As regards the matter of smoking in the autopsy room, the pathologist doesn't indulge for the simple reason that he has both hands full and even a Houdini couldn't manage it. You might start off with a lighted pipe, but you would find it inconvenient to light it again and would very quickly discard it. Once in my early training days I was called upon to perform a rush autopsy at 2 A.M. Thinking that I would be all alone, I lighted my pipe before starting and was blissfully puffing away as I proceeded at my untimely chore. The door slowly opened and in the doorway appeared the same chief who had previously detected the blood spot on my elbow. He was attired in a top hat and full-dress suit, as was the custom in those days when you went to the opera, and he obviously was just returning from a performance. Seeing a light in the windows of the autopsy room at that unusual hour, he had decided to investigate.

Not a word did he say. He simply turned on his heel and departed. Nor did he say anything the next day. But about two years later, when a discussion came up about the impropriety of clinicians smoking in the autopsy room, he suddenly glared at me and said, "How can we expect the clinicians to stop smoking if even our own staff members break the rule?"

However much general standards have deteriorated, this prohibition is generally respected: no objectionable foreign material is ever introduced into the body of an autopsy subject. I can think of only one exception. I once knew a pathologist who, although his sense of decorum was impeccable in every other way, was in the habit of inserting a sheet of folded newspaper on top of the organs after they were restored to the body. When I asked him why he did this he relied, "It makes it easier to sew up the skin incision, and besides we use only *The New York Times*, and who could possibly object to that!"

5

A Digest History of Pathology

To MAKE this book intelligible to the average reader, it will be necessary to define the science of pathology more exactly and in greater detail. It is my intention to try to describe the interrelated discoveries in lens-making and medicine that made the development of pathology almost inevitable. It is also my purpose to relate how the need for pathologists originated, what their early activities were, how they went about making contributions to medical knowledge, how they affected the practice of medicine and, finally, what unexpected developments have produced their present status.

Of course I don't intend to write a formal history of

pathology. I won't furnish the names and numbers of all the players, let alone all the dates and places. I have no doubt that there is need for a scholarly and traditional history of the science, but this large and time-consuming labor requires a judicious-minded historian of temperate disposition. I do not qualify. I am reliably informed, however, that a very eminent pathologist with a remarkable gift for writing has been assembling data during the past few years for a definitive history of pathology in America. If my own efforts arouse the interests of readers in this forthcoming book, I shall be more than satisfied.

In my opinion, the single discovery that has had the greatest impact on the development of modern medical knowledge was the demonstration of the fact that the tissues of the body are composed of small, uniform and recognizable living structures known as cells. This discovery became possible only after the compound microscope had been invented, for cells are too small to be seen with single magnifying glasses. The microscope made it possible to develop a logical understanding of organic disease, and from this understanding almost all other medical discoveries have subsequently been derived. The microscope removed the cataracts of ignorance from the vision of doctors. It was as essential to medical advance as the discovery of the wheel was to mechanical progress.

The earliest microscopes were clumsy, cumbersome affairs, hard to get much light through and hard to keep in focus. It took more than fifty years after its development in the eighteenth century before it became widely used as an instrument for medical investigation. Virchow is the man who had the greatest influence in establishing microscopy as a valuable technique. We pathologists venerate him as our founding father and patron saint, and we believe he has had a profounder effect on the health of more people than any other man who ever lived, not even excluding Pasteur. It is possible, even probable, that if Virchow had not lived, someone else would have made the same discoveries, but we can't be sure. It is not quite like saying that once ocean-going ships were built, the discovery of America by somebody became inevitable. The microscope might have remained a freak instrument of no practical use if the discoveries of Virchow and similarly minded persons had not made other doctors eager to learn microscopy. As a result, the construction of microscopes underwent rapid improvement, and they became available in ever-increasing numbers. But even those constructed at the end of the nineteenth century were crude affairs by present-day standards. These instruments are museum pieces now, and trying to use them truly increases your admiration for the accomplishments of the early microscopists.

As the microscope became more workable and complicated, techniques were slowly evolved for preparing thin slices of tissues and staining them with suitable dyes so that the cellular structure of tissue might be carefully scrutinized. These techniques are now highly standardized and used all over the world.

The revolution in the orientation of medical science has been so profound, it is difficult to believe that Virchow's great book on cellular pathology was first published only a hundred years ago. Anatomical dissection had shown doctors before Virchow that in various diseases certain of the organs underwent marked changes in appearance. But of the way these changes were produced they had no idea. They knew nothing of how tissues grew, nothing of the composition of pus, of the nature of inflammation or tumor growths, of the healing processes or scar formation. Study of slides under the microscope made possible knowledge of these things. It disclosed the principles involved in reactions of tissues to injury. The average doctor finds it hard to conceive of a medical world in which these things were not understood. We take them for granted like the Ten Commandments, the Magna Carta and the Declaration of Independence.

Prior to the development of the microscope as a research tool, diseases were identified, classified and treated chiefly by the symptoms they produced. Tuberculosis, for example, was generally known as "consumption," referring to the wasting away of patients. Yet the symptoms of different persons with the same disease can vary tremendously, and very different diseases can produce identical symptoms. Under such conditions medical diagnosis was almost meaningless. Treatment was directed entirely at alleviating the symptoms. There was no other approach.

Microscopic study of diseased tissues made it possible

to develop an entirely new classification of disease based on the organs involved and the nature of the changes themselves. From this it soon became evident why patients with certain diseased organs had certain symptoms. Physicians in those days spent a great deal of time in the autopsy room trying to correlate symptomatology with pathological findings. They learned that groups of symptoms might reveal the nature of the disease involved. A group of symptoms occurring in a patient as a result of some underlying process became known as a syndrome. The method by which physicians evaluated the significance of various symptoms in arriving at a clinical interpretation became known as differential diagnosis. Many volumes devoted to differential diagnosis were published and widely read. Accuracy in diagnosis improved by leaps and bounds, but only doctors who checked on the post-mortem findings available in every case became skillful at this game.

Perhaps I had better explain more exactly what is meant by differential diagnosis. Abnormalities detected by the techniques of physical examination, such as tapping a patient's chest or listening to his heart with a stethoscope, are called physical signs. Each sign or symptom found in a patient may be the result of one or several diseases. By more or less tabulating the various diseases that could produce each sign or symptom found in any one patient, and then deciding which disease best accounts for the greatest number of signs or symptoms and leaves the least number unaccounted for, the doctor often is able to discover the nature of his patient's illness. This process is called differential diagnosis.

It soon became evident that trained and experienced post-mortem dissectors and microscopists were essential to obtaining accurate pathological information. Some doctors spent more and more of their time performing autopsies and less and less time with living patients. And thus the specialty of pathology developed. Soon some medical men were willing to devote all their time to evaluating the pathological changes discovered in the dead. There wasn't much money in it, but there was a lot of satisfaction and not a little prestige.

This sequence of events took place most dramatically in Germany and Austria, where the first full-time pathologists practiced, and in these countries medical science became pre-eminent—so much so that doctors from all over the world eventually flocked there to learn the "new" medicine. Those who did so gained a great advantage over their colleagues when they returned home. Pathology automatically and irresistibly gained an important status in medicine. Eventually American doctors went to Vienna or Berlin for the express purpose of becoming pathologists. They brought back to this country the knowledge and techniques acquired abroad. The most renowned of these was William Welch. Originally American pathology was almost strictly an import. Even to this day, its study is more heavily stressed in the medical curriculum of European schools than in this country.

From the beginning there has always been the problem of how the pathologist could earn a living if he gave up clinical practice. No one could expect the relatives of the dead to pay for post-mortem examinations. In fact, they had to be persuaded to consent to them at all. Hospitals and medical schools generally did not have the funds to build laboratories and pay the needed personnel. The early pathologists did their own technical work. Even up to twenty years ago, a famous Boston pathologist, Frank Mallory, insisted that all his students learn technical methods as part of their training in pathology.

The early German pathologists earned their keep by lecturing and writing scientific articles. This encouraged them to talk frequently and, since they were paid by the word for their articles, to write long, repetitious and often very trite papers. Indeed, pathologists sometimes got the reputation of being very verbose and dabbling with the trivial. And this reputation was often richly deserved. It was really the first black mark scored against the science of pathology. Even to this day, no one is more apt than the pathologist at "dissecting the obvious and squeezing the last drop out of a foregone conclusion," and generally he compounds his offense with a profusion of lantern slides. The pathologist might be a learned and invaluable colleague, but he was sometimes a bit of a bore. He had to be, or his income would suffer.

In this country, the early pathologists worked chiefly in medical schools or in large, progressive and well-endowed hospitals that could afford to pay them straight, if meager, salaries. Sometimes these pathologists augmented their income by working part-time in smaller institutions that could not afford a full-time pathologist. This practice still goes on. In large cities there are pathologists who cover as many as a dozen hospitals. It is highly remunerative but a dreadful way to live. For a long time pathologists remained few in number and poorly paid, but they had a compensating eminence in the field of medicine. The names of famous pathologists like Pick, Aschoff, Councilman, Klotz, Erdheim, MacCallum, Wolbach, and many others equally outstanding were known all over the medical world. Every leading medical school of the early nineteen-hundreds had a renowned pathologist. It was more than a coincidence. Frequently the influence of the pathologist built the reputation of the school. Today's top pathologists are almost as anonymous a group, as far as the public is concerned, as former Nobel Prize winners. Sometimes they are not even known to everyone by name in their own institutions.

It would seem, in fact, that the pathologist once preferred to be a little apart. There are a number of family dynasties among them, but a surprising number of the early American pathologists never married or, if they did, produced only daughters. I don't believe that any aberrant tastes were involved other than perhaps a dislike for domesticity. One famous pathologist is said to have carried on a prolonged and ardent affair with a celebrated prima donna of the time. Another is reputed to have kept a succession of mistresses and not always one at a time. The tendency, if it was that, has largely disappeared and the current crop are good solid family men for the most part and have plenty of male offspring.

The pioneer pathologists made their discoveries in many ways, but microscopic technique was usually involved. They might, for instance, recognize that certain special kinds of tissue damage in various organs tended to develop only in a few individuals. By studying the clinical records of these patients, they might discover that their illnesses had been very similar. It would then become obvious that a newly recognized and distinctive disease entity had been uncovered. The next time a patient with a similar group of symptoms came along, the doctors, having learned about the autopsy findings in the cases, would be in a position to detect its presence while the patient was still alive. Very often the disease became known by the name of the pathologist who had described it. For example, Pick's name is attached to an inflammatory disease involving the lining surfaces of the major body cavities and also to a peculiar disturbance of fat metabolism in children.

The list of famous achievements is long. Aschoff described certain heart changes in rheumatic fever and first formulated the concept of the reticuloendothelial system. Councilman did pioneer work on the pathology of amoebiasis and yellow fever. Erdheim discovered why the largest artery in the body sometimes ruptures spontaneously. MacCallum discovered how the calcium of the blood was regulated and the life cycle of a malarial parasite. Wolbach discovered the nature of pathological changes in several vitamin diseases and typhus fever. Ewing spent most of his life cataloguing the various types of tumors.

I could go on and on, but I'm afraid such condensed single-sentence summaries of a productive life's work are absurd. Whenever I read the obituary notice of a distinguished person, I am depressed by how few words are required to sum up his accomplishments. He was the man who first grew a nerve in a tube, it will say, and thus unveiled tissue culture to the scientific world. Sometimes it will say of an octogenarian that he was the man who caught the pass that beat Purdue in 1902, leaving you with the feeling that the next sixty years of his life were strictly anticlimactic. The pioneer pathologists did more than make isolated discoveries; they created and gave direction to a new school of thought on the causation of disease.

Some modern medical thinkers object strenuously to having diseases named after men. They think that the name of a disease should indicate its nature, but for some reason they never seem to object to totally illogical but time-honored names of diseases such as measles, smallpox or leprosy. I don't agree with them. I think it very fitting that a disease become a memorial to the man who first resolved its nature. The names of these discoverers pass all too quickly into oblivion, and encyclopedias have no space for them after filling the priority needs of famous athletes, actors and politicians.

Remarkable changes in the specialty of pathology have taken place in the past twenty-five years. Originally the pathologist's main function was to perform autopsies. The scientific yield from these was at first rich. But the inevitable law of diminishing returns eventually set in. The rich vein of new discoveries began to dry up. Pathological knowledge became a part of the education of all medical students and very old hat. Autopsies became more and more a routine investigation concerned primarily with the findings of the case in hand, findings that are usually without any new wide implications concerning the nature of disease. This sort of thing happens to many, if not all, new sciences. There is the initial discovery period, usually associated with the development of new techniques. Then follows the exploratory phase, in which new observations are described and classified. After this a period of flowering ensues in which there is much theorizing, until the assimilated information is thoroughly sorted out, regrouped and digested. Finally there is the period of stagnation and status quo, when real progress stops unless some fresh technique or unexpected discovery gives the science new impetus. This has been the history of many of the special fields of medicine. They grow old, wither and sometimes die.

But pathology did not quietly lie down and die. It simply underwent certain transformations that happened so subtly that even the pathologists themselves were often unaware of them. When morphological bacteriology ceased to be an investigative science, the routine diagnostic tests were turned over to trained non-medical personnel who became known as bacteriologists. The original investigative bacteriologists turned to other spheres and even changed the name of their calling, possibly so that they would not be mistaken for technicians. They are now known as immunologists, immunochemists, microbiologists and, if they are persuasive enough, even as experimental pathologists. The same thing might have happened in pathology. Non-medical workers might have occupied the field except for the fact that it is not possible to train ordinary technicians to recognize the nature of changes that occur in diseased tissue. The role of the pathologist changed gradually from teacher and investigator to diagnostician. As an interpreter of the changes that have occurred in diseased tissue, the pathologist is often indispensable in the handling and treatment of patients. There are all sorts of diagnostic tests with different degrees of reliability. Most of these can be performed by trained technical personnel, usually under the supervision of a pathologist. These tests are classified as chemical, bacteriological, hematological and serological. Such tests are done in rule-of-thumb fashion, following exact prescriptions almost like recipes in cooking. The answers are quantitative and frequently mathematical. The persons performing the test need know nothing of what ails the patient. It is up to the clinician to interpret the results.

The tissue pathologist, on the other hand, gives no numerical answers. He has to know as much as possible about the illness of the patient whose tissue he is examining. He must be able to recognize and identify abnormal cells and abnormal cell arrangements, tell where they have come from and, most important of all, predict what will happen to the patient. Stripped down to bare essentials, it is the pathologist's job to tell whether an abnormal swelling is due to tumor growth and, if so, whether the tumor is innocent or potentially fatal. This is the important determination that the pathologist is called upon to make during every one of his working days. Often when a tumor has become large its nature is obvious without microscopic examination, but the doctor tries to discover tumors in the earliest stage possible, when they are small and removable, and it is at this stage that microscopic study by a trained pathologist is needed. Not too infrequently, the pathologist is unable to make an exact diagnosis, but he is always being pressed to do so by the attending physician. When the pathologist does make a definite diagnosis, his decision is usually accepted and acted upon. He can't afford to make many mistakes. In most hospitals there is a rule that all doubtful growths be examined by biopsy before they are surgically extirpated. This means that small samples of the diseased tissue must first be removed and studied microscopically before the diseased focus is excised *in toto*. All sensible surgeons obey this rule, or sooner or later they find that they have subjected a patient to a drastic and unnecessary surgical procedure.

It should now be evident why technicians cannot do

tissue diagnosis. It requires a thorough training in medicine. In fact, the pathologist has to be familiar with all fields of medicine. The specimens he receives come from all parts of the body and are sent to him by specialists of every kind, from dentists to orthopedic surgeons. Some schools have offered Ph.D. training in pathology, but holders of such degrees have seldom become skillful pathological diagnosticians. The pathologist's interpretation of what is going on in diseased tissue is always an opinion based on the evaluation of what he sees. Very often he is unable to give a definite answer, but when he does, he has to be right. A competent pathologist leaves the guesswork out of his diagnoses.

It would be idle to pretend that any great talent is required to become a competent pathologist. All that is needed is a reasonably good visual memory and long and continuous application under experienced supervision. The elementary details are learned quickly; the finer details are acquired only after years of study. A pathologist gets so that he recognizes tumors the way one recognizes acquaintances. Often he finds it difficult to explain why he thinks a tumor is malignant or has arisen from a certain type of tissue, just as it is often difficult to describe accurately a person's face even if you know him well. Naturally some persons are more adept than others at learning how to recognize pathological processes under the microscope. A few are incapable of learning the art at all, even after years of study. A working pathologist concentrates so much of his effort on learning about tissue changes that he often becomes absent-minded about almost everything else. It is almost as though he trained himself not to waste any of his memory on anything unrelated to pathology. Perhaps he's the prototype of the absent-minded professor so familiar in all disciplines.

The pathologist must not only spend long years learning his art but also keep in constant practice, like a violinist or professional fighter. Even a month's vacation can cause him to lose a little sharpness, and after long layoffs, even proficient pathologists become very stale. A high order of intelligence is not required of the diagnostic pathologist, and is possibly even a handicap to him. Persons with lively or creative intelligence are not attracted to this specialty today as often as they were in the past. The art is much more like that of coffee tasters, wine sniffers or piano tuners than anything else I can think of. Pathologists sometimes begin to lose their diagnostic skill as they grow old, usually without realizing it themselves. This has happened to many pathologists whom I have known and the change usually starts around the age of sixty. I believe it has to do with failing eyesight or loss of association of visual images.

As the pathologist's role as a teacher and investigator deteriorated, his influence and importance on medical-school faculties also declined. But at the same time his value in diagnostic work increased. Once the nature of organic disease was understood, a host of ingenious laboratory tests were devised to test the function of different organs or to determine the presence of abnormal agents in the body. Most of these tests were devised by clinicians trained in chemistry, physiology, hematology and immunology, and not by pathologists, but few of the tests would be in existence today if the pathological nature of disease had not first been illuminated by pathologists. Such tests have taken much of the guesswork out of clinical diagnosis. They have become as important as the study of symptomatology. Learning to be a doctor today is chiefly a matter of learning what tests to order, what not to order, and how to interpret the results. The inferior doctor always seems to order a great profusion of tests, but somehow manages to ignore or omit the one that would establish the correct diagnosis. All these tests, grouped together, are called clinical pathology. The supervision of clinical pathology has become one of the major functions of most hospital pathologists. Financially speaking, it's the most rewarding thing they do.

As clinical pathology developed, hospitals found it necessary to enlarge their laboratory quarters and increase the laboratory work force. Since the services of a pathologist were necessary to diagnose surgically removed specimens, hospitals began to hire full-time pathologists to run their entire laboratory service. The demand for pathologists increased as their key status in medical schools declined. At first, hospital patients could ill afford to pay for a battery of laboratory tests, and the hospitals could not finance an elaborate laboratory. Hospital insurance changed all that. Now the hospital laboratory is like the football team of a university. Its profits help support the entire institution.

Doctors who have gone into pathology with visions of an academic career but with modest financial aspirations frequently find themselves in a commercial atmosphere, and if they are good businessmen as well as pathologists, they may become extremely wealthy. The less attractive a pathology job is from the scientific point of view, the larger salary it is likely to offer. A competent pathologist has to be practically bribed to accept a rural hospital position where he knows he will find little scientific stimulation and will be isolated from the rest of the pathological community. In many a small town the hospital pathologist is the highest-salaried man to be found, a fact that sometimes startles the local citizenry. It may exasperate the hospital manager, whose own salary is usually much smaller. If he is small-minded, he may try to annoy the pathologist in many petty ways, but never quite enough to make him resign, because his replacement will probably demand an even higher salary.

Increasing numbers of medical-school graduates are going into pathology and there are now many thousands of trained pathologists throughout the country, though thirty years ago there probably were fewer than two thousand. Yet the impression is of a shortage, since the number of positions available for fully trained pathologists, as well as for residents and assistants, has increased faster than the supply, and many positions remain open for years. The specialty of pathology is now a more lucrative profession than it has ever been before.

But the pathologist is not especially in demand to perform autopsies. He is wanted primarily for his ability to run the clinical laboratories and to make diagnoses on tissues removed from patients when they are still alive. The one diagnosis he makes that puts him on the indispensable list is the determination as to whether tumor growths are benign or malignant. His other diagnoses are generally of secondary importance. The prosperity of pathologists thus rests on a very slender support. The day some clever chap devises a successful test-tube method for determining the presence or absence of a malignant growth in a patient, the pathologist's income may begin to decline. For in some ways a well-trained chemist is in a much better position to run the clinical laboratories than a tissue pathologist. Once the cancer diagnosis problem is licked, the hospital administrator will be tempted to defy the pathologist's associations and hire a Ph.D. in biochemistry as his top boy in the laboratory. Test-tube methods for the diagnosis of cancer are announced almost weekly, but none has so far proved its worth.

This brief summary should suffice as at least a sketchy idea of the functions of pathologists and how the need for them in the care of sick people originated. It should also be evident that the activities of the pathologist almost inevitably place him in constant contact with all the services of a hospital. Occasionally his job gets him involved in controversies with the various categories of doctors who run these services. It has also earned for him that dubious distinction of sometimes being referred to as the doctor's doctor.

It is my evil intention to explore in future chapters the nature of the relationships that have developed between pathologists and their clinical colleagues. In so doing, I shall be writing from a highly biased point of view and will probably say many things that clinicians may regard as offensive if not untrue. So before I presumptuously put on the mantle of judge and critic, I should like to pay tribute to the practicing doctors and to acknowledge my own great personal debt to their accomplishments. It is my belief that my own career as a perpetual patient provides me with special qualifications for examining the activities of doctors. I have an insight that the average healthy, and therefore incompletely informed, pathologist does not possess. For I have examined both the professional and the patient's side of the coin.

6

A Career as a Patient

M O S T pathologists know their clinicians (a general term I use to denote all practitioners of medicine) only in a professional or social way. They know them from the surgical specimens they receive, from the bodies that they examine at autopsy and from the complaints that reach them about the inaccuracy or tardiness of laboratory reports. These contacts I have also had, but I have had additional and unusual opportunities to watch clinicians in action. In fact, they have worked out extensively on my person. This, I feel, makes me eminently qualified to discuss the relationships between clinicians and pathologists.

Some people choose their own hobbies, others have

their hobbies thrust upon them. My hobby is being a sick patient. It is not one of my own choosing. I will match against that of any pathologist in the land my record for number and variety of major operations performed upon me, for number of hospital admissions and for length of stay in hospitals. I have been treated by eye doctors, ear-nose-and-throat doctors, general practitioners, internists, chest specialists, cardiologists, gastroenterologists, proctologists, urologists, general surgeons, thoracic surgeons, orthopedists and even dermatologists. Actually, I have been treated by almost every major variety of doctor except pediatricians and neurologists. I hear the echo of someone saying those are the ones I really needed.

I should have died in 1941, 1947, 1950 and 1955. I have been treated for everything from cancer of the roof of the mouth to profuse bleeding from the large intestine. I have had seven major operations performed on me and each one for a different condition. I have been admitted to hospitals sixteen times, the longest stay being nine months. Every time my name is mentioned in Blue Cross circles, a dozen highly placed officials promptly swoon. I have received every kind of anesthetic, from ether by the open-drop method to spinal block. Ether is the most unpleasant because you reek of it for two days. Spinal anesthesia is the most frightening because you think you are permanently paralyzed until at length you find you can wiggle your big toe. Pentothal is the nicest, not much worse than taking a sleeping pill.

I have had every conceivable instrument inserted into every conceivable orifice, by maestros and by crude and clumsy novice residents. I do not particularly recommend the bronchoscope. Its passage is painful, and moreover the whole proceeding is a highly undignified affair, down to the last bitter insult when, with your head bouncing around on the lap of a perfect stranger, you are asked to cough lightly just as you have decided that even breathing is a doubtful necessity.

Levin's tubes in your gullet are not so distressing, but they have an effect of cumulative discomfort. By the third day they are downright offensive. Cystoscopes and proctoscopes make effective instruments of torture, particularly in the hands of the inept, which class includes a goodly number of interns and residents. A T tube in your bile duct has its own peculiar and far-from-minor vexations. But speaking as a connoisseur, I believe the aftermath of an open thoracotomy under artificial respiration is in a class by itself. We initiates speak of it as the "long cut." Nothing is so calculated as this surgical treat to make mere living seem—for seven days—such a dubious affair. The only thing that saves you is that on each of the first seven postoperative days you feel just a little less beyond the pale, and on the seventh day life becomes worth-while again, almost as though someone had just stopped hitting you on the head after you had decided that being hit on the head was the normal way of life.

I dramatically began my professional career as a pa-

tient when I was still in my thirties. I had had a few
earlier skirmishes with disease, but these were strictly
beginner's encounters. One evening, quite unaccount-
ably, I discovered I was bleeding very profusely into
my intestine. I was alone at the time, and I didn't know
exactly what to do as I became progressively weaker and
realized that I was about to go into a state of shock.

I managed to get to the telephone and ask the house
operator to get in touch with Dr. S., a bicycling-type
surgeon whom I knew reasonably well and whose ability
I respected. It was just a name that came into my
rapidly clouding sensorium. Doctors are such irresponsible types that it took all of fifteen minutes for Dr. S.
to negotiate the considerable distance to my apartment.
My message had reached him while he was presiding as
toastmaster at a banquet. He found me in the bathtub,
collapsed and bloody. The ambulance, which he had in-
stinctively ordered before he left the banquet hall, arrived a few minutes later and I had the first of quite a
few sunny-side-up rides of this nature. No one ever
forgets his first ambulance ride. I can even remember the
tilting maneuvers that were necessary to get the
stretcher into the house elevator.

Dr. S. rode with me to the hospital where we both
worked, namely dear old Bellevue. This hospital means
different things to different people. Some love it greatly
and some not so greatly. Basically I belong to the latter
group. But in Bellevue emergencies are just another
routine and they are handled with incredible speed,

efficiency and aplomb. It is a tradition going back over a hundred years. Ring the alarm and the old fire horse yawns once and then leaps into action. There may be other hospitals that can respond in this fashion, but I rather doubt it.

Even the willfully eccentric and autonomic elevators enter into the spirit of the thing. The elevators in this ancient institution have nervous systems of their own and are therefore called autonomic rather than automatic. They make up their own mind just when they will run and where they will stop, which during regular hours is hardly at all. The queen of the autonomic elevators is situated in the old city morgue and it seldom runs at all in the daytime and never stops at the floor of your choice. But if you sneak up on it in the dead of night, you will discover that it is shuttling back and forth at a rapid speed and of its own volition, no doubt carrying the ghosts of the many departed who have passed through this building on their way to limbo.

I was wheeled through the admitting-office area without so much as a pause, and in no time at all was unclothed, draped and in the operating theater. Meanwhile word had spread rapidly through the hospital, in which I was well known for my amiable nature and unswerving good disposition, and throngs of doctors and students began to collect. They sauntered by in clusters very much like a Saturday-night social promenade on the town square of a Central American town. Privacy I had none, and to add to my humiliation I was placed in a most embarrassing position in order to be properly examined. I didn't even have enough blood left in me to manage a proper blush.

My surgical friend approached me waving an electrocautery like a magic wand. With the end of this he touched a bit of angry mucosa in the appropriate place and pronounced, "Henceforth you will bleed no more." And believe it or not, I've never bled since. This incident has firmly convinced me that this surgeon has supernatural powers acquired no doubt by dabbling with black magic and evil spirits.

The next morning I was awakened at a predawn hour by a nurse's aide and found myself in what turned out to be a side room off the main surgical ward. My first impression was that it was a garage for the ambulance. The décor was not exactly elegant, although the walls still had some large patches of paint that had not yet peeled away. I was weak and feeble but still alive. The nurse's aide proceeded to give me a bed bath and rather startled me by congratulating me on the cleanliness of my ankles. I realized that I would have to adapt to my environment. Then she tidied up the room a bit, and when she came to the ash tray, which contained a fair collection of cigarette stubs, inquired politely, "Are you saving these?" By this time I had entered into the spirit of the thing and so I replied, "But of course."

Still later she returned with a bowl of oatmeal that had been laced, by way of preparing me for X-ray examination, with a large portion of barium. I had never heard of this concoction and found it most difficult to negotiate. It tasted like liquid plaster of Paris, and for all I know, perhaps this is what it was. I can swallow a beaker of barium as well as the next fellow, but it is no good at all by the spoonful.

In spite of these mishaps, I improved rapidly, and on the third morning decided to get out of bed and go to the washroom on my own. It was a cold wintry morning and day was just dawning. As I passed through the corridor, I glanced into the main ward and saw the head nurse standing by a bed patiently feeding spoonful after spoonful of breakfast food to an ancient, unkempt, crippled, trembling and repulsive derelict of a patient. It is a sight I have ever since been unable to forget. The thought of it takes the fine edge off of my native cynicism. What can you do about a harsh world that nevertheless has Bellevue nurses in it?

In the decrepit washroom I found a large congregation of patients lounging about, for this was the only smoking and social center of the ward and was heavily patronized at all hours. Most of the plumbing didn't work at all, but there was a permanent trickle from one of the washbasin taps. I found that the patients were very amiably disposed toward me because the orderly who held the very vital and profitable toilet-paper concession had had second thoughts about the matter when he learned that a doctor was on the ward as a patient, and had installed a brand-new roll for free. Life as a Bellevue patient gave me an insight into things that up to then I never even knew existed.

After I had left the hospital, it suddenly occurred to me that the surgeon must have paid for the ambulance that transported me. I was embarrassed when he adamantly refused to let me repay him, claiming I had done him a great service by getting him out of a very dull banquet. After a little rationalization, I came to the conclusion that while there are a lot of people who have been operated upon by big-name surgeons for free, there are not many who can claim that the surgeon had to pay for the privilege. This made me feel a lot better.

My next major episode of illness came about a year later. I awakened in the middle of the night with the feeling that a convulsive Mexican jumping bean had been let loose somewhere in my midsection. The pain was very severe, but I was determined not to seek help until the next morning. Since I am a reputable pathologist, I didn't have a pill of any kind in the house, let alone one that would control pain. Many sick people will struggle along with a pain all day, hoping it will go away and refusing to call a doctor. Then in the dead of night the same pain becomes insupportable and they demand immediate attention. A doctor is understandably annoyed when the patient who has called him at an unseemly hour admits very freely that he has had the pain for at least twelve hours. I didn't want to put myself in that category.

The next morning I went to the hospital where I had once served my residency and consulted a contemporary of mine who had a reputation for being very thorough. He put a blood-pressure cuff on my arm and presently said thoughtfully, "How long have you had high blood pressure?" I said that I had never had high blood pressure. He tapped my chest and said with a long face, "When were you treated for tuberculosis?" I said I had never had tuberculosis. He listened to my heart and wanted to know how long I had had rheumatic heart disease. I said heatedly that I had never had heart disease. Finally he examined a urine specimen and said, "I suppose you know you are a diabetic." "Stanley," I replied, "I'm a very sick man. Quit horsing around."

So Stanley finally settled down to business and admitted what we both knew, that I was having renal colic. This came as no great surprise to me. I had recently returned from a trip to Central America where my entire fluid intake for several months had been restricted to Coca-Cola, which I used to wash my teeth, and to tequila, which was both cheap and sterile. In a hot tropical country, such a limited fluid intake invites the forming of kidney stones.

The reason for my foolhardiness was that on my first day in Costa Rica, the very courtly Spanish gentleman and doctor who ran the medical service had taken me around the wards of the hospital. We came upon two young doctors who were vociferously arguing in Spanish at the bedside of a tiny, shriveled lady who, in spite of her appearance, was probably only forty-five. I couldn't understand a word of the argument, but as it reached its climax one of the doctors shouted something that unmistakably meant, "I'll show you who is right," and left the bedside in a lather. He soon returned carrying the most enormous syringe I have ever seen. It looked like one of those clysters in a Hogarth print. He promptly plunged the needle through the old lady's abdomen, hardly taking aim, and a look of great satisfaction appeared on his face as he withdrew an endless quantity of thick gray pus from what was obviously a huge amoebic abscess of the liver. The old lady seemed to grow more cheerful by the moment. I was so impressed that I immediately made a resolution not to drink any unboiled water during my stay.

My cure progressed very efficiently and uneventfully although I had to submit to an operation to get rid of the stone. I was obviously receiving very expert care and I forgave my doctor for his introductory badinage. But on the day after the operation he came into my room and asked, "Did you really mean what you said when you were coming out of the anesthetic?" I pressed him to tell me what outrageous breach of good behavior I had committed, but he only gave me his own repulsive version of a Mona Lisa smile. For this I have never forgiven him.

I left the hospital quite well but with empty pockets. At this time I had not been foresighted enough to join Blue Cross. As I walked to the nearest subway entrance, I read the words, "For of the most high cometh healing," carved into the cornerstone of the building. I wondered why someone had thought it necessary to rub it in.

Following this episode, I had a series of illnesses too numerous to detail, but in each instance I was fortunate to be in the hands of expert physicians, and I triumphantly survived all my ailments. One of the highlights of this series included an operation, performed by a really top-flight surgeon, for a badly misbehaving gall-bladder. When the time came for my discharge, he presented me with a quart-sized bottle of vitamin pills that he had no doubt pilfered from the hospital pharmacy.

This little gift would probably have cost me fifty dollars if I had purchased it in the usual fashion. It was a purchase I would not have made. I had a low opinion of the need for vitamin pills at the time, based on some experiences in trying to produce vitamin deficiency in animals. To do this I had to feed them strange concoctions, and it had always seemed to me that an ordinary healthy person with an average diversity of tastes in food stood a mighty slim chance of being deficient in vitamins. But I did admire the chartreuse color of the pills. It seems to me that the artistic qualities of modern pillmaking have been overlooked in the emphasis on the pills' curative effects. Many people who pay an exorbitant price for a bottle of pills feel that their enforced contribution to medical research may be a bit too formidable. They should remember, however, that they are patrons not only of science but also of the arts. Some of the most extravagant artistic productions in America are in the literature that the pharmaceutical houses send to doctors. This literature is handsomely adorned in order to persuade the doctor to look at it before tossing it in the wastepaper basket. Meanwhile the commissions that many very talented young artists receive often tide them over periods of pecuniary embarrassment.

90

I went to stay with friends for my convalescence and as I unpacked I was tempted to try one of the vitamin pills. The taste was immediately familiar. It was identical to that of a special kind of bonbon for dogs known as "yummy," which I had once sampled in an unsuccessful attempt to find out why they were so attractive to dogs. My friends owned a Chesapeake retriever named Katie, of which I was very fond. Since it was the time of the year when retrievers lose their second heavy winter coat, Katie had a threadbare appearance. I might go so far as to say she had developed a few sores. Katie's appetite was of the broad-spectrum variety, but she was especially partial to ice cream, eggshells and yummies. I tried a vitamin pill on Katie just to see if she too could recognize the taste. She responded enthusiastically, and research-minded as always, I fed her the entire contents of the bottle at one sitting, or perhaps I should say jumping. I am pleased to report that within twenty-four hours Katie's sores had entirely disappeared and that her coat has remained sleek and lustrous ever since. No longer do I speak with disdain of the efficacy of vitamin pills. Of course I wouldn't want to take any myself.

I suppose I should be ashamed to confess that I have never paid a fee to a doctor. When I first started out on my career as a constant patient, it wasn't even considered good form for a doctor to suggest making such a payment to another doctor. The latter would have been offended. But times change and the dollar becomes ever more respectable. Nowadays the problem has been partially solved, since we can join Blue Shield, which assures us that the doctors who treat us can at least expect the modest insurance fee without embarrassment to anyone.

There was an intermediate period in which the doctor-patient was expected to offer and try to insist on paying his doctor bill. The kind of doctor whom I always chose would have none of it. Perhaps it worked out this way because I have always been highly discriminating in the kind of doctor I have consulted, and quality doctors are still not the kind that will readily accept fees from their colleagues. I have always been able to select good doctors, because the nature of my work keeps me well informed on the inside workings of medicine— "inside" in a sense that Gunther never dreamed of.

It has always been considered good practice for a doctor to give his doctor some sort of gift, but a problem to know what. Originally such gifts were intended merely as tokens of appreciation and it didn't matter how much they cost. Later on, as doctors began to have second thoughts about accepting free medical care, doctor-patients felt obligated to offer a fairly substantial and expensive expression of gratitude. I remember once confiding to a department-store saleslady that I was looking for a suitable gift for my doctor. She didn't know that I was one myself and was highly indignant at the idea, possibly because she had just paid a large doctor's bill herself. "Good grief," she said, "you mean to say you are going to give a *gift* to the robber?"

Following one of my early illnesses, I once naïvely presented a book (I believe it was Cushing's life of Osler) to one of my doctors. He turned it over curiously, like a chorus girl who has just been given a second book but is determined nevertheless to be polite about it. After this deflating experience I would call the doctor's secretary and try to get some hints as to what the doctor might like. I soon discovered, however, that the secretary almost invariably selected something that she wanted for the office. Finally I confided my problem to another experienced doctor-patient. "Nothing to it," he informed me. "Liquor is the international medium of exchange between doctors, and besides it is income-tax free." I have never gone wrong since.

No doubt it is a necessary thing that the custom of not billing other doctors is falling into discard. There is no reason why an exceptionally competent doctor should be penalized financially when other doctors take up the time that he would have spent with paying patients. All the same, there was something warm and noncommercial about the old system. Recently I heard a story about doctors whom I don't even know in an institution in which I have never worked. It is probably a fabricated story, but it nevertheless reflects some of the scuttlebutt that goes on in the medical world.

In this tale, a doctor had been operated upon by a classmate who had become a highly successful surgeon. A few days later the surgeon stopped in to see his patient and said, "John, I'm off to Florida for a vacation and will probably not have a chance to see you again. If it's all right with you, perhaps you had better settle up with me now."

"Why, of course, Jim," said the patient. "I insist on paying the regular fee. I wouldn't dream of letting you operate on me without paying for it. What would you consider a suitable amount?"

"Well, John," the surgeon said, "I usually charge three thousand dollars for this kind of operation, but for you, since we're old friends, I'll make it fifteen hundred."

Yes, indeed, I liked the old system better.

It should be apparent that doctors are no different from anyone else when it comes to afflicting their friends with endless accounts of their sufferings as patients. Whenever I transgress in this manner with some other doctor who has had illnesses of his own, he can try to retaliate. But my position as champion is difficult to challenge. Nowadays when I sit down at the luncheon table in the doctors' dining room and say, "Did I ever tell you about my operation in 1945?" everyone present hastily excuses himself. Authors, I suspect, have hidden as well as professed motives for writing books. In my case, it provides me with a new opportunity to talk about my ailments.

The most recent major illness of my career was one that is regarded as an occupational hazard of pathologists. I have known or heard about at least fifty persons, including myself, who contracted tuberculosis while engaged in the business of performing autopsies. It is not the great hazard that it once was, I am happy to say.

The marvelous new cures, notably isoniazid and streptomycin, have taken a good part of the lethal sting out of
the disease. Even in the days before these drugs were discovered, most pathologists recovered. But the cure was
a long-drawn-out and tedious affair. Relatively speaking, I believe there have been many more cases of tuberculosis among pathologists than among the medical personnel working in the tuberculosis wards. This I feel
gives me some justification for relating my own experiences with the disease.

7

The Magic Molehill

I STRONGLY suspect that not many members of the Nobel Prize awards committee ever had tuberculosis. Otherwise the first users of the most effective antituberculous drug, isoniazid, might have received one of their awards. To me, perhaps because I have personally benefited therefrom, this drug is one of the really great curatives of all time, second only to penicillin. Pathologists used to see almost daily in the autopsy room the dreadful ravages that this disease could produce. Isoniazid and other drugs that act similarly have all but tamed it.

Once I had occasion to examine a chronological list of all the winners of the Nobel Prize in medicine. I was mortified to find that there were several names I had never even heard of and that the discoveries for which the awards were given did not seem so imposing as they must have in the past. I questioned a number of my associates and was relieved to find that I was not the only ignoramus. And I was also amazed to learn that many illustrious medical scientists, both living and dead, whose names immediately occurred to me, have never been so honored. An intriguing book could be written on the scientific achievements of nonwinners of this award. Such a book would be particularly soothing to the geriatric set of distinguished scientists and help them through the trying fastigium of Nobel Prize fever.

The effective drugs now available for the treatment of tuberculosis have changed it from a mountain to a molehill among the infectious diseases. Some of the shrinkage took place during the period of my own cure. Isoniazid had been introduced, but its efficacy had not yet been fully established. I took it because the older, fully proved drug, streptomycin, was no longer capable of restraining my own particular bug. I have some personal malice toward streptomycin, because I received enough of it to impair my appreciation for music, even though it did not make me deaf. I can no longer distinguish high-frequency notes and therefore get no pleasure out of listening to classical music. Much to my distress, this became evident during my long convalescence, but I continued to put Chopin's nocturnes and Schumann's sonatas on my record player, chiefly because they made my visitors feel so sorry for me.

Pathologists generally contract tuberculosis by cutting their fingers while handling tuberculous specimens in the autopsy room. Weeks later a small hard lump will appear at the site of the cut. Most of the time the lump remains for many months without getting any larger. Sometimes the infection spreads along the tendons of the hand, or large lumps may appear at the elbow region or in the armpit. We almost always wear rubber gloves to protect our hands, but a sharp scalpel point can easily penetrate the covering. The older pathologists often felt, mistakenly, that their constant exposure to all sorts of infections made them highly resistant, and I can remember some who refused to wear gloves at all. There was a time when I would foolishly handle tuberculous specimens barehanded. This was particularly unwise, for my experience indicates pathologists are much more vulnerable to tuberculosis than are the medical personnel who take care of patients on the tuberculosis wards. As a matter of fact, the latter hardly ever seem to contract the disease, probably because proper precautions are maintained.

Many years ago, I acquired my first skin nodule or tubercle, as it is called. I was trying to impress the barefoot autopsy virtuoso, Raffaillo, with my own speed and dexterity, knowing full well that he would be taking me off later on when I left Costa Rica. This nodule finally healed and I doubt that it was the cause of the lung tuberculosis I acquired much later. Apparently I exposed myself in a much more asinine fashion. We had a leaking brine icebox in the laboratory. The cooling pipes in the back of the icebox compartments were sheathed by a regular glacier of ice that had formed on them over the years. Encased within this were numerous tuberculous specimens that thoughtless residents had once placed in the icebox for future study. They then proceeded to forget about them and some specimens had remained there for years. (This is perhaps just another reason why I do not always cherish charitable thoughts about residents.)

I decided foolishly to clean out this awful mess and spent a weekend leaning into the various icebox compartments and cracking up the ice mass with a long chisel and mallet. Tubercle bacilli can live a long time in ice, as I was shortly to discover. A few months later I developed a bad cough that was different from any I had ever had before. The most disturbing feature was that the material I coughed up had a sweetish, slightly fermented fragrance, such as one used to detect on tuberculosis wards. I put off doing anything about it as long as I could, but finally gave in and consulted the best chest doctor I knew. When she had taken one look at my chest under the fluoroscope, I could tell from her reaction that I was in for plenty of trouble.

The day after I was admitted to the hospital a junior colleague came rushing into my room, his face wreathed in smiles, and announced happily, "Your sputum is simply *loaded* with tubercle bacilli." This startling piece of news failed to arouse any feeling of joy. In fact, my friend's attitude had me bewildered. "Why, you ungrateful wretch," he said, when he saw my lack of enthusiasm for his wonderful revelation. "We were all sure you had cancer." It took me quite a while to appreciate his point of view, but of course he was right. Tuberculosis is something you can cure.

At the present time, the most trying period for a patient with tuberculosis is the first few days after diagnosis. You realize that you have contracted something that not even the most expert doctor is going to get you out of in a hurry. Up to this point in my varied career as a patient, I had always shown good judgment in coming down with dramatic but nevertheless rapidly curable ailments. The transition from a normal way of life into that of a chronic invalid is hard to take.

After a few days in the hospital, you rapidly become adjusted to your new restricted conditions of life. The thing that helps you accept your fate with resignation is the realization that everyone is suddenly full of the milk of human kindness. You are pampered with all kinds of special attention and lead a sheltered and protected life. If the truth be told, it is not an unpleasant position in which to be. I suppose it must sound very shocking, but I look back at the period of my convalescence as an agreeable episode in my life. When, however, I visit some successor who is holed up in the same room that I had, I find it difficult to believe I was able to survive nine months in such an atmosphere. Yet the new victim usually has the same resigned and cheerful attitude that I once had most of the time.

I escaped most of the harrowing experiences that used to be the fate of persons with this disease. It was

no longer necessary to wait a long time to find out
whether I would recover or get worse. Nor did I have to
wait very long to see signs of improvement. After a few
days on the drugs, the fever and cough had gone and I
was completely without symptoms. From then on it was
chiefly a question of living under the conditions that my
doctors prescribed until they pronounced me cured.
Nevertheless, I got a pretty good dose of what is called
absolute bed rest during the first three months. I wasn't
even permitted to toss around in bed too vigorously. The
granting of "bathroom privileges" became a momentous
occasion.

Life becomes largely a matter of sleeping, eating and
reading, interrupted by a constant stream of visitors. In
this respect the doctor as a patient is in a much better
position than most patients, because he convalesces in
his natural environment. It is so easy for doctor friends
to stop in and see you in the course of their ordinary
duties that one seldom lacks for company except during enforced rest periods. Furthermore, I began my
cure during the hot summer months and mine was one
of the few air-conditioned rooms in the hospital. I never
knew whether my visitors came to see me or to cool off.

Very soon you become aware of a remarkable fact.
People can easily be divided into two categories, those
that are good hospital visitors and those that are poor
ones. It doesn't seem to matter much how well you know
them or how much you may enjoy their company under
normal conditions. There are just some people whom
you may love dearly but who you wish would depart

after a brief visit. Then there are others who seem to fit into the environment and whose company you can enjoy for hours, even though you know you will hardly ever see them again after you leave the hospital. I was never able to fathom the secret of this particular division of mankind.

It was my particular good fortune to have as a neighbor in the next room a most congenial doctor. He was made of sturdier stuff than I, and during the first few weeks he had a very good effect on my morale. In addition, he was two or three months ahead of me in the progress of his cure, so I could benefit greatly by his example and counsel. He was particularly helpful in advising me how to get through the first dreadful days after a lung operation. Among other things, he taught me how I would have to cough. It's a difficult art and I used to practice it before the operation. The method consists of giving a series of tiny little coughs in rapid succession, working up to the last big one that will clear your air passages. If you are thoughtless enough to give one big cough without this preliminary effort you feel as though you were coming apart at the seams.

On the morning of my own operation, the surgeon leaned over my stretcher as, well sedated, I was about to be wheeled into the operating room. "How do you feel?" he said.

"Fine," I replied.

"By the way," he said, "which lung am I supposed to operate on?"

For once in my life I couldn't think of an appropriate

answer. As I came into the operating room, I saw the anesthetist, bellows in hand (this was in the days before machines had been developed to blow air into your lungs during such operations), and I knew he would have to sit there for three or four hours and breathe for me by hand. It was the student I had once been unkind to! Thus do our sins return to haunt us.

The tuberculous patient comes to be on very intimate terms with the nurses and their aides, particularly the latter, since they do so many menial services for you. I was greatly distressed when the nurse's aide who gave me the most superb back rubs was arrested for selling narcotics she had stolen from the hospital. Her replacement had once worked as a maid in a large Park Avenue household in which the master had the habit of eating three eggs for breakfast. The new nurse's aide obviously believed that three eggs for breakfast constituted the last word in high living. So she insisted that I have this number every morning. I obliged her, and further indulged freely in other naughty foods that are supposed to bring on heart attacks, as did all the patients. Yet heart attacks on the tuberculosis wards of a hospital are practically unheard of.

Persons with tuberculosis occasionally become depressed or irritable, but not nearly so often as those who suffer from other chronic diseases. One day I was chatting with one of the older doctors, who had spent most of his life caring for tuberculous patients and was wise about their reactions. A nurse came into my room to tell him that one of the patients had just committed suicide. My visitor was willing to bet that the suicide probably had not had tuberculosis, and he proved to be quite right. The patient *had* had a chronic disease of the lungs, but not that one. Tuberculous patients rarely end their own lives.

Some doctor-patients become so acclimated to their way of life that the ones taking care of them sometimes fear they may actually protest being discharged. Some of us become absorbed in hobbies, such as knitting, building high-fidelity sets or putting together elaborate jigsaw puzzles. I used to work on hypothetical chess problems, not that it ever improved my game very much. It is true that the exact date of leaving the hospital often becomes very unimportant, and if the doctor suggests that you stay on a few weeks after tentative discharge date has been set, you are usually not profoundly disturbed. Yet when the time comes to emerge from your tuberculous cocoon, you accept the inevitable.

I was given a two months' supply of isoniazid pills on my discharge from the hospital. During my hospital stay I had become very adept at taking them and had learned how to swallow the required six at a time with no trouble at all. Pill-taking becomes a nuisance once you are up and about again, and I soon began to cheat. When each two months' period was up, however, I would return to the hospital for a new supply. I would ask the doctor each time if it was necessary to continue taking the pills. She would reflect for a moment and say, "Well, I guess you had better continue it for another couple of months." I would take the new supply and discard them. Two months later the same process would be repeated. This might have gone on indefinitely, but quite by accident I learned that the doctor had remarked, "I wonder how long that bird is going to go on taking pills." I suppose she felt that as long as I felt insecure enough to keep asking about the pills I had better continue to take them.

And this is the latest chapter in the story of my many illnesses. I have gone into it in great detail in order to give some idea of the scope of my personal indebtedness to the medical profession. Its practitioners have done more than right by me. Any forthcoming complaints I shall make have to do with my professional relations with them as a pathologist and are offered with my fingers crossed. I do not know when I will have to call on them for help again.

The doctor as a patient learns an aspect of medical care about which he is not ordinarily too well informed. It is one thing to observe patients and quite another to be one. I believe that all young doctors ought to be subjected to the various procedures and treatments they prescribe. They might thereby acquire a more tolerant attitude toward the so-called difficult patient. In the case of surgeons, this might be a little impractical, but every surgeon should subject himself to one major operation before considering himself fully qualified to perform them on others.

Of course all my doctors without exception have been the best of the best. This statement requires a little amplification. When a patient is satisfied with the services of a doctor, he promptly elevates him to the position of a divinity. Doctors as patients are no different from anyone else in this respect. Naturally I feel that my opportunities to evaluate the performance of various doctors are better than those of the average patient. To deify his doctor is not a bad thing for the patient. It gives him great confidence in the doctor's ability and wisdom, and unquestionably helps in effecting his cure. "My doctor has never lost a case," says the doting and probably not too well-informed patient. Any doctor who hasn't lost a patient, with the possible exception of dermatologists, hasn't had much of a practice.

Most doctors are able to shrug off the role of minor deity. On a few it has a disastrous effect. They accept the role and all the perquisites that go along with it. Pretty soon their partnership with God becomes a little irksome and they begin to demand priority rights in the duality. Such supreme beings do not make jolly company, but do no particular harm unless they get elected as officials of some large medical society. The pathologist can detect this personality change early in the game and is wary of doctors who have assumed the role of God. They are apt to be very highhanded with us, as though we were minions of the Devil and therefore natural enemies. Nevertheless, I beg their forgiveness for the blasphemy of writing this book.

CHAPTER

8

My Particular Friends
the Surgeons

CATS and dogs can learn to live harmoniously in the
same household under conditions of discreet neutrality.
There is no reason why surgeons and pathologists cannot get along together amicably in a hospital—and we
frequently do. But the pathologist is primarily a cogitator and the surgeon a man of action. Of necessity,
we may learn to cooperate, but we can never fully inte-
grate. When the cogitator misguidedly wanders into a
career in surgery, he does not thrive. When the man of
action becomes a pathologist, an even drearier fate
awaits him. He generally ends up writing textbooks.

I use the term "pathologist" to refer to my own particular variety. I do not accept the qualifying terms

107

that, as I have explained, are used to describe various activities of the pathologist, such as "diagnostic," "tissue," "morphological," "routine," or "hospital." The men who taught me were known simply as pathologists, with no qualification of the name, and I refuse to relinquish the right to use that name unless I am compelled by court action. Let the miscegenated splinter groups who dabble both in pathology and in other fields of medicine at the same time use the modifying terms. A British pathologist who is a winner of the Nobel Prize may boast that he has not performed an autopsy in thirty years. To me this disqualifies him as a pathologist, but then the English have always had peculiar ideas about the usages of the English language.

Many years ago, when I was a medical student, a story was current about an applicant for an internship in surgery. This applicant, so the story went, was a brilliant student with more than his share of good looks, personal charm and high character. In addition, he came from a socially prominent family, was a famous athlete and a talented amateur artist and pianist. It was taken for granted that he could obtain any internship that he wanted. But when he was interviewed, the professor of surgery told him, "I'm dreadfully sorry, I can't appoint you. You are exactly the type of man I want, but I never accept candidates who are scholastically at the top of their class."

This story was of course fictitious, but it pleased me all the same. Years later at a medical dinner I found myself seated next to the professor of the story, and thinking to amuse him, I told him the anecdote. Much to my surprise, he readily confirmed it as true in essence if not in fact. He said that when he had first started selecting surgical interns, he had not discriminated against exceptionally good students, but he found that they almost invariably were unreliable in the operating room and he had decided not to gamble on them.

This is not meant to imply that all good surgeons are dumb. Far from it. There are all kinds of intelligence, and the kind that makes for a good surgeon is not one that leads a student to get high grades. As a matter of record, many medical students who receive high grades in school do not become distinguished doctors later in life. A good surgeon does not necessarily have to be speculative by nature. He must be willing to accept the consensus on doubtful issues and, as the gamblers say, play the percentages in his medical decisions. Most of all, he must make fast, sensible decisions and never vacillate. The surgeon who hesitates or procrastinates in the operating room is one of doubtful value.

He also has to have the good muscular coordination and fast reaction times that are essential to a skillful technician. He must have the temperament that will help him retain his skill in the most trying times of stress or emergency, even when he appears to lose his temper. These are exacting requirements but by no means peculiar to surgery. Almost any "money-player" type of athlete, especially a shortstop, would make an excellent surgeon. By the law of averages, persons with these talents are not too often gifted in other intellectual pursuits. It would be too much to expect nature to be that bountiful. When surgeons go in for hobbies, they usually pick something in which they can utilize their mechanical skill.

I do not mean to imply that surgeons are not well-rounded types. As a matter of fact, they would, taken together, probably go further in the nonmedical world than any other group of physicians. Businessmen recognize a kinship with surgeons. When a newspaper reporter interviews a business tycoon, eventually he gets around to the question, "What line of work would you have gone into if you had your life to live again?" At this point the tycoon flicks a little ash from his expensive cigar and replies, "Well, sir, I would have been a surgeon." And a misty look, no doubt, comes into his eyes. If he doesn't say this, he ain't no proper tycoon. I have never heard of one who replied that he might have become a pathologist. If one ever did, I am sure that the stock of his company would suddenly decline in value.

The basic temperaments of surgeons and pathologists offer a good study in antithesis. The pathologist seldom likes to make up his mind on controversial issues, will occasionally reverse himself, depending on his mood, or offer half a dozen suggestions and refuse to decide among them. Nothing is so calculated to irk surgeons, many of whom would prefer a doubtful pathological diagnosis on which they could proceed to none at all. No surgeon has been overtly angry at me for an incorrect diagnosis (and I admit to a few whoppers), but plenty have been irritated because I refused to make any flat diagnosis at all.

Though the average surgeon and the average pathologist regard each other with mutually felt reservations, there are plenty of exceptions. Some of my best friends have been surgeons. But the surgeon is apt to think of the pathologist, especially the old-fashioned autopsy-performing one, as an egghead and a pretty poor specimen of manhood, who is probably secretly a communist. On the other hand, we pathologists regard the average surgeon as a possible lowbrow or an insensitive type who is probably privately a fascist. This was perhaps more true in the old days when pathologists did most of their work in the autopsy room. Now that many of us have lost our prestige as out-of-this-world intellectuals and are diagnosticians who command a fairly decent salary, the surgeon is coming to be more tolerant of us and we of him. We may not have quite got up into the surgeon's financial brackets, but at least we are out of the class of people who might feel they had to speak softly about income.

Nowadays the surgeons reserve their suspicions for the biochemists, microbiologists and the other really high-class dolichocephalists of medicine. It is the ten-grant egghead researcher whom the surgeon finds most incomprehensible. I should add here that I feel researchers should be classified like polo players, since in many respects the polo player is the counterpart in the world of sport to the researcher in the world of medicine. A researcher who carries ten research grants at the same time is equivalent to a ten-goal man in polo. Thus the ten-grant egghead. Surgeons are more likely to be football or fight fans.

Occasionally I attend research seminars in the vain hope that I may improve my mind and acquire a little scientific culture. At one such recent seminar, the investigator who was presenting his experimental work said something that sounded like this:

"We were then able to planchette the eluate and thus derivatize the potassium moiety. We were very excited when the results were charted on semilogarithmic paper. We obtained a skew curve that, when extrapolated to the abscissa, clearly showed that the ion-exchange component is segregated into two compartments, a fast and a slow one."

As he went on with his presentation, I could sense a feeling of mounting interest and excitement in the audience. The investigator was asked questions that indicated conclusively that the listeners understood him fully. "How do you know that there are only two compartments? Couldn't there be a lot of little ones?" someone asked. "Ah, that is the question that worries us. It will take years of work to settle it," the investigator responded. And, he might have added, many more research grants.

I sat there in silence, uncomprehending but impressed, not even permitting the scurrilous words "So what?" to enter my mind. I looked about hopefully for some other square who might not have been able to get

112

with it, and spotted a surgeon. Surely, I thought, his grasp of the subject could not have been more profound than mine. Up spoke the surgeon: "This is very exciting work but what do you hope to prove ultimately?" The magic thread was broken. The Philistine had intruded.

After a momentary pause, the investigator, with just a show of annoyance, replied, "If this technique can be adapted to other problems, we may be able to synthesize insulin so that it will cost less than five cents a pound."

For all I know he may be right. But this story I think illustrates a difference between surgeons and pathologists. The surgeon is made of sturdier stuff—he wants answers.

The advances made in the basic-science laboratories percolate through to the surgeon with relative slowness. But when they do, he becomes most enthusiastic. Twenty years ago the internists were very hot on vitamins and on studies of the blood electrolytes. Now they are still interested in but rather blasé about such things. The surgeons, however, have become intrigued now and are giving the old vitamins-and-electrolyte balance a real workout.

A hundred and fifty years ago the surgeon was the barber's most inept and least-promising pupil. Today he is often the barber's best-paying customer and stands very high in the pecking order, not only in the medical world but in the community at large. The surgeon has earned the right to his ever-growing prestige by his own accomplishments in developing operating skill and devising ingenious surgical procedures. He gives due credit to the anesthetists, who have made it possible for him to explore the most hidden and vital recesses of the body, and to the discoverers of antibacterial agents, who have reduced postoperative infections to a minimum. He is less likely to delve further back and to acknowledge that it was the understanding of the pathological nature of disease processes that provided the rationale for the operations he now performs. It is the kind of debt so self-evident that it is easy to ignore.

The average general surgeon performs a surprisingly small range of operations. He makes the bulk of his living on the three H's—hernias, hemorrhoids and harmless appendices. If he can interlard a few removals of gallbladders for stones, breasts for cancer, stomachs for ulcer, and uteri for fibroids, he is well on his way to prosperity. Once he has set up in practice, he seldom has the opportunity to perform the spectacular operations that he may have learned in his training days, the ones you read about in the papers.

The successful surgeon can command formidable fees for his services. Sometimes it is difficult for the public to understand why he should charge so much. The surgeon justifies his fees by reference to the sacrifices he had to make to acquire his skill and the long years of privation during his first years of practice, when he struggled along with few patients. Actually, it is the public that sets the size of the fee. People are willing to pay high for the services of a "name" surgeon and I don't blame them. Surgeons' fees are pretty much the same thing as the prices a successful painter can demand for his work. A good picture costs no more in time and materials than a poor one. The same holds true for surgical operations. There can be a great deal of difference in the performances of good and of mediocre surgeons.

I do not envy the surgeons their prosperity. As far as their professional activities are concerned, it is probably very desirable that they be well paid. The very rich, if they are so minded, can afford to be strictly scrupulous and idealistic. Sometimes articles appear in popular magazines claiming that a large number of unnecessary operations are performed, and the implication is that surgeons are shady characters. These articles may be written by the kind of science writers who turn out the cancer-scare articles that have sent susceptible people scurrying to their doctors.

No group has a monopoly on either vice or virtue, and in my dealings with surgeons I find them in general to be honorable men, a good cut above the average. If they occasionally seem to be a little premature or eager as far as performing operations is concerned, it is due to overzealousness and not to greed. Surgeons understandably believe in operations, the way pathologists believe in autopsies. If they see any chance of improving a patient's health by an operative procedure, their fingers become itchy. They are impatient of long trials with conservative medical therapy. There are, however, innumerable occasions when the surgeon refuses to operate, on the ground that the operation is too hazardous or impractical, even though the medical consultant or the patient urges it. I have worked in institutions where surgeons donate their services or are full-time employees who are not paid according to the number of operations they perform. Yet these surgeons seem to have exactly the same attitude about the indications for surgery as do those in private practice.

This is not to imply that internists or pathologists always agree with surgeons as to what constitutes adequate justification for an operative procedure; in fact, surgeons do not always agree with one another. As a pathologist, I find myself in dissent on numerous occasions. I am opposed to what is known as palliative surgery unless it is quite clear that life will be significantly prolonged or made more comfortable. A palliative operation is one that is performed, not with the hope of effecting a cure, but to relieve the patient's symptoms —such as unrelenting pain—or to prolong his life. This is a very legitimate form of surgery, but when it comes to pass that I perform an autopsy on someone who only a short time before has had palliative surgery, no one is very happy about it. The borderline between palliation and euthanasia surgery is not always too clear-cut.

I am also opposed to diagnostic surgery where a major procedure is involved and where the chances are exceedingly remote that information helpful to the patient will be uncovered. Diagnostic surgery, it should be self-evident, is an operation performed chiefly to establish the correct diagnosis, with the hope that some effective treatment can then be prescribed. It is not always pos-

116

sible to be certain whether such procedures are done to satisfy the curiosity of the doctors or to help the patient.

These are the kinds of operations one could argue about. Whether they are deemed necessary or uncalled-for is a matter of judgment rather than of ethics. As I have said, I think the notion that surgeons perform unnecessary operations to collect the fees is largely untrue, at least in the medical circles in which I have traveled. It is not the pathologist's business or responsibility whether or not a surgeon performs an operation unless, perhaps, the decision is based largely on the pathologist's diagnosis. I shall digress to give an example of how pathologists have become involved in one type of surgical operation that has been performed more frequently in recent years than ever before. This story should be educational to hypochondriacs.

What with one thing and another, the cervix of the human uterus is subjected to periodic irritation and it often becomes slightly inflamed for prolonged periods. Eventually the cells of the mucous membranes become peculiar in appearance and sometimes they turn into cancer cells. Telling the difference between peculiar cells that are not cancerous and true cancer cells has always been the pathologist's major job. Long ago, when pathology was chiefly a science and not a diagnostic technique, highly skilled pathologists studied individual cancer cells very carefully, looking for some constant change in structure that would identify the cell as a cancer cell and not merely as an abnormal-looking noncancer cell. They concluded that cancer cells did not have anything that normal ones did not have.

Many years later some investigators, who were primarily anatomists, observed in examining vaginal smears of women with cancer of the uterus that the cancer cells looked distinctive and different from normal cells in their special kinds of preparation. They had the advantage over the older pathologists in reaching this conclusion, because they did not know too much about cancer or about the wide variety of changes that can occur in injured cells that are not cancerous. It would be possible, they concluded, to diagnose early cancer of the cervix of the uterus by examining cervical smears that could be prepared easily and looked at by trained technicians. To a large extent, this has proved to be the case. At least it is possible by examining such smears to make a very good guess as to whether cancer is present or not, although usually such diagnoses are confirmed by cutting out bits of tissue for a more conventional type of microscopic study.

In a cancer-conscious community, the examination of cervical and other types of smears has grown to be a specialty all its own. I doubt that the initiators of the technique ever realized its potentialities. At first, pathologists were loath to become involved, chiefly, I think, because these smears have a fuzzy appearance under the microscope. I always feel as though I were reading tea leaves on the infrequent occasions when I am inveigled into looking at them. Pathologists spent many decades devising techniques that prepare cells in ways that sharply define their details, making them clear and brightly dyed with contrasting stains. Most of us carry on an unending battle with the technicians who produce them. I strongly suspect that my own technicians live in mortal terror that someday I will beat them with a stick when they present me with an imperfect section.

Gradually most pathologists have become resigned to participating in this splendid new science of exfoliative cytology, as this smear-searching method is so aptly called. It has made almost everyone happy. The science writers who inform the public about it feel they have done their duty in enlightening their readers. For a small fee and not much inconvenience, women are reassured that they do not have cancer, and the few whose smears turn out to be positive are restored to health by an operation that relieves them of some of the inconveniences of an actively functioning organ. The doctors are happy, the laboratory becomes ever more solvent, and the hospital management is pleased. Everybody, in fact, is happy except me. I am unhappy, not because I have to look at such smears, but because I occasionally find myself in a losing battle with the gynecologists. The smear has been reported positive for cancer, but I may find only doubtful changes in the subsequent biopsy examination, the study of a bit of tissue.

Only once did I emerge triumphant from such a battle and the event has changed my whole attitude toward the United Nations. I now think it is a splendid organization and not the least bit precancerous. A woman delegate of a foreign nation, who was determined to take advantage of all aspects of our superior standard of living while she was here, had a cervical smear examined that was reported as positive for cancer. I found only a few suspicious changes in the small bits of uterine tissue that were subsequently removed and sent to me for study. The gynecologist was disgusted with me for quibbling about the diagnosis. The woman agreed to have her uterus removed, but insisted on postponing the operation until she had settled some personal affairs at home. By the time she returned, the suspicious area had disappeared. The gynecologist, being a diehard, insisted that his biopsy had cured her. Whenever I see a statistical study which claims that nine out of ten women can be cured of uterine cancer, I wonder how many were "cured" as was the United Nations delegate.

Let me leave surgery for a moment to make a general qualification. It should be apparent that I am a hopeless reactionary who resists progress wherever it rears its ugly head. This, too, is in the tradition of old-line pathology. There are still a number of ancient and venerable pathologists around. They wear overcoats that are just as ancient as they are, coats that time has shaped to their forms and covered with a kind of greenish mold, and hats that look like floppy tobacco leaves. In fact, they look like old Wall Street bankers. These old-timers used to pose for their photographs with a beat-up single-tube microscope of obsolete design prominently displayed. It was an affectation, but one that I liked. The up-to-date modern scientist wouldn't use such an instrument as a doorstop or a nutcracker.

Pathologists of the younger generation do not accept the idea that pathology is no longer a field for discovery. When they write papers, they list a battery of newly devised staining techniques they have used to study tissues, thus proving that they are up to the minute and progressive. But when you read their papers in detail, you often find that the fancy new stains have contributed precious little to their results. I confess to a weakness for so-called special stains, but I like them chiefly for their aesthetic value. Once I had occasion to consult about a difficult slide a pathologist who was at the time generally considered to be one of the two best surgical pathologists east of the Mississippi. He was known privately as the Sachem of 68th Street. I brought along some specially stained slides. He looked at me in disgust. "Do you mean to say that you, too, use these fancy stains?" I felt ashamed, as though I had betrayed the calling of pure and classical pathology.

To return to my particular friends, the surgeons, I suppose I have given the impression that the country is filled with crackpots who want to get themselves cut open. This is not the case. For every hypochondriacal patient who courts an operation, there are a dozen resistant ones who refuse to be operated on even when it is imperative, often with tragic results. But by and large the public has lost its fear of surgery, just as it has lost its fear of being hospitalized. Operative deaths have dwindled to the vanishing point. Three fourths of the patients who come to autopsy have old surgical scars of one sort or another.

Perhaps I have also created the impression that surgeons and pathologists are unduly chummy in the hospital. In many cases they remain discreetly aloof from each other. But there is one procedure that brings them together—the business of frozen sections. A frozen section is one that is prepared during the course of an operation and interpreted immediately by the pathologist. The usual microscopic slide takes from twenty-four to forty-eight hours to prepare and is diagnosed, obviously, after the operation. For the frozen section, a small piece of tissue is quickly frozen with liquid carbon dioxide, cut into very thin slices on a special machine known as a microtome, and stained and examined while still wet. The whole process takes only a few minutes, but the preparations are vastly inferior to the regular ones and often difficult to interpret. Such sections are relatively thick, cloudy and poorly stained, compared to the slowly prepared permanent sections, which are processed by passing the tissues through many solutions that improve their cutting and staining qualities. The interpretation of frozen sections generally involves guesswork, and pathologists are trained not to guess. Obstinate surgeons are sometimes incapable of grasping this simple point. It is difficult to convince them that if the easily prepared frozen sections were good enough, we would not go through the complicated and expensive rigmarole involved in producing our regular specimens.

Once frozen sections were only rarely requested during operations, usually in connection with the removal of suspicious-looking masses from the breast. If the frozen section reveals cancer, the surgeon will proceed while the patient is still anesthetized, and do a much more extensive operation calculated to prevent the recurrence of the tumor. If the mass is reported as benign, only a small amount of tissue is removed. The patient is thus saved the bother of two operative procedures. There can be no doubt that frozen sections can be an important and helpful procedure in many cases, particularly with small, hard breast tumors whose nature cannot be told by just looking. Most of the time, an experienced surgeon can tell by mere inspection whether the growth is an innocent or a malignant one, and the preparation of the frozen section becomes almost ridiculously pointless. Nevertheless, having been alerted for the frozen section, usually at 8 A.M., the pathologist will go through with it, since it is a simple procedure. This helps remove any feeling of having answered a false alarm. Pathologists are a little like firemen. We get annoyed by too many false alarms.

In recent years, surgeons are requesting more and more frozen sections on all sorts of things. In fact, it sometimes reaches the point of absurdity. Some of this is due to the fact that many of the current generation of surgeons receive inadequate training in pathology. In the old days, your old Halstedian surgeon spent a year in the pathology laboratory as part of his training. Later only six months were required. In the last few years, even this requirement has been dropped. In my opinion, this is a mistake. Surgeons with a background of training in pathology can be more skillful than pathologists in recognizing the nature of abnormal tissues that they handle and inspect during an operation. A competent surgeon can tell dead tissue from living tissue and inflamed tissue from tumor tissue. The ignorance in this regard of the new crop of surgeons can be appalling. Some of them have to call the pathologist to the operating room repeatedly to learn from him things that they ought to know themselves. Peering over their shoulders and seeing a mass of rubber-gloved fingers and blood clot, we are supposed to advise them. They may be technically just as skillful as surgeons who have received adequate training in pathology, but such surgeons will never operate on me.

Surgeons who have had some experience in pathology know the limitations of the frozen-section method and are much more sensible in their requests for this procedure. Furthermore, if the frozen-section report doesn't square with what they see, they will ignore it and use their own good judgment. It takes a bold and confident doctor to ignore a laboratory report, and only the really good ones can do it and get away with it. Badly informed surgeons accept all laboratory reports at their face value. To them, a frozen-section diagnosis is just as reliable as any other. Such surgeons get into the habit of ordering frozen sections to satisfy their curiosity during the operation, not because the result will change the operative procedure they are performing. They seem to believe that the only reason why pathologists don't do frozen sections in every case is that they are lazy and uncooperative. There are even a few surgeons who think that by having frozen sections cut from the edges of a growth they can find out if the whole tumor has been removed.

There are certain famous clinics in which frozen sections are cut routinely during every operation. This is done, in my opinion, chiefly for window dressing or subtle advertising. The implication is that these institutions spare no effort to help the patient. Rich people are able to afford such luxuries and usually expect a little extra something for the big fees they pay. This practice has given the surgeons all over the country the feeling that if they want to be on a par with the surgeons in these famous clinics, they, too, had better ask for plenty of frozen sections. It is a little like a chef who thinks that if he puts paper panties on his lamb chops, he is running a superior kitchen.

There is one redeeming feature about the pointless frozen section. It helps keep the hospital solvent. Most hospital patients today have some kind of hospital insurance. The insurance companies pay a flat fee for all laboratory tests done on each of their insured patients. This payment is much less than the full rate for every test. If they paid those, they would go bankrupt. One thing that is generally not included in the flat payment is the fee for frozen sections. The hospital makes an extra twenty-five dollars every time its pathologist performs an unnecessary frozen section. Blue Cross officials please take notice.

A surgeon's reputation is based largely on his performance in the operating room under the glare of bright lights. It is difficult for him to conceal incompetence. Surgeons with great reputations are invariably ones with unusual proficiency in operating technique. There are, however, many extremely skillful surgeons who never acquire great renown. There is a thespian quality to a surgeon's work. Personally, I prefer those who follow the precepts of Billroth to those who follow Stanislavsky. It is much harder to judge proficiency in a pathologist. He renders the last opinion and often there is no way of checking up on it. If a pathologist is so inclined, he can often conceal his errors. If he has called a benign tumor malignant and nothing happens to the patient, he can say that the surgeon was successful in removing the growth or that the radiologist has destroyed it. Or he can say, "Just wait a few years and it will come back." If the patient never returns, he is just lost sight of. If the pathologist has called a malignant tumor benign, he is a bit more on the spot, and in the best interests of the patient he prefers to avoid this error—just to be on the safe side. But even if a tumor called benign grows back, he can claim it has undergone a malignant transformation. You cannot, therefore, always judge the ability of a pathologist by his diagnostic reports.

Much is written about the very rich and very poor having the advantage over the middle classes in the kind of medical care they can obtain. The implication is that poor people in charity hospitals get better care than does the person of average income who pays his own way. This is partially true, but mostly hogwash. Many a nonpaying patient, who would never dream of having his hair cut in a barber college, has nevertheless had his gallbladder taken out by a beginner in surgery who has never had his hand on a gallbladder before. But when it comes to the accuracy of pathological diagnosis, the very poor easily come out as well as any other group. In fact, it is to their advantage that the pathologist does not have to consider the status of the patient or his relation to his doctor in arriving at his interpretation.

It is a common human failing to pass judgment on all our associates. This is a form of egotism that even the most modest person finds it difficult to escape. The pathologist's job is to judge the specimens that the surgeon sends him, but being no better than anyone else, he soon finds himself judging the surgeon himself. In doing so, he uses different criteria from anyone else. He is influenced most by the specimens he receives. Good surgeons produce handsome tissue specimens. There is often an artistic, well-sculptured quality to the well-dissected specimen that proclaims the fact that the operator is a pro. A pathologist working in a small hospital where the same group of surgeons operate all the time, gets so he can identify the surgeon simply by looking at the specimen, just as an art critic can tell a Mondrian from a Feininger. We pathologists prefer surgeons of the old classical school, who produce cleanly dissected, pretty specimens, to the impressionist, who brings forth gory, ragged, and crushed abstractions. We say that the latter "has no respect for tissues," which is about the most damning thing you can say about a surgeon. And if a uterus arrives in two parts— brother, there is nothing more to be said!

Surgeons quite justifiably can become very much annoyed if the pathologist's report gives any indication that the operation performed was an improper one. There was once a time when a pathologist might worry about losing his job if he dared call an appendix normal after an influential surgeon had made a preoperative diagnosis of acute appendicitis. Nowadays it is accepted that this is a legitimate mistake if it is not made too frequently. In any case, appendicitis has ceased to be as potentially dangerous as it once was, and no longer is an appendectomy performed for every unexplained bellyache. The doctor can now dose the patient with antibiotics and wait to see if the pain goes away.

Surgeons are often tempted to open and examine, before sending them to the laboratory, the specimens they have removed. This is understandable, although strictly speaking it is against the rules of the American Medical Association, which decrees that the specimen must be delivered to and examined by the pathologist. Surgeons frequently remove gallstones from gallbladders and give them to the patient as keepsakes. This may sound a little silly, but I myself keep a precious little crystalline black gem in my desk. This object I once delivered myself from my kidney with as much pain and effort, I believe, as any pregnant woman ever had in delivering her own child. I am as proud of it as an oyster of the pearls it produces.

The difficulty is that when the pathologist receives an opened gallbladder without any stones, he is expected to write in his report that it contained them. Occasionally one receives a perfectly normal gallbladder and the surgeon says it contained stones. We generally meet this problem by stating, "Specimen is received opened and contents removed." But some surgeons are not satisfied. I know one who has hardly spoken to me for years because I once refused to include, on his word alone, gallstones as a part of my diagnosis. Nevertheless, I keep a large jar of unclaimed stones on hand and am prepared to furnish any shape, size and color to patients who are anxious to have them.

The American Medical Association has a set of rules that governs the handling of surgical specimens. These must be abided by in all approved hospitals. The purpose of the rules is to maintain a high standard of ethics among surgeons. For the most part, rules are not needed, but the fact that they do exist helps curb nefarious practices. One rule I have already cited—that all specimens must be sent to the regular laboratory of the hospital in which the operation is performed. Another is that each hospital must have a tissue committee that reviews all operations of a dubious nature, such as sterilizations, operations in which no tissue was removed and ones in which there is marked discrepancy between the preoperative and pathological diagnoses.

In practice the tissue committee actually turns out to be a farce in which the surgeons do most of the complaining, chiefly about tardy pathological reports, the wording of the diagnoses and even the color of the requisition slips used. There is seldom any occasion to call a surgeon on the carpet. But the mere fact that the tissue committee exists is a very excellent thing. It helps destroy that old Hippocratic illusion that everything that goes on between a doctor and his patient is a private affair concerning no one else.

Surgical pathology is a necessary but pretty dull pastime. There is a great deal of repetition in the specimens we study. Most of the time the diagnosis is known or suspected before we examine the tissue. On occasion the pathologist is able to discover an unexpected and curable disease process, and this affords a brief moment of triumph. The surgical pathologist's chief source of mental stimulation comes in trying to identify certain rare processes, chiefly obscure tumors, of which there is a great variety. Certain tumors are composed of cells that are amnesia victims, just like actors in English movies. They have forgotten where they came from and have lost all identification marks. These are often the most malignant growths. Generally we diagnose them as "tumors of unidentified type," but nevertheless spend much of our time trying to track them down. Groups of pathologists often meet and swap speculations about their various amnesic tumors. These groups should be called Missing Tumor Bureaus. It is usually impossible to be certain of the identity of these growths, even after many pathologists have reviewed them. But by following the progress of a tumor in the patient, its true nature—sometimes months or years later—is at last unfolded.

It is because pathologists cannot always recognize such tumors that clinicians get the impression we don't know our business or are fakers. The only real faker is the pathologist who claims to be able to recognize them. One scoundrel of a radiologist once shopped around with a batch of obscure tumors among the ten leading pathologists in the New York area. There was a great deal of difference in the opinions expressed by these various experts. He then tabulated his results and published them as a scientific paper to prove that pathologists were unreliable. I cheerfully admit that there are many growths I can't identify, and if shown the same slides weeks apart, I may offer a very different opinion the second time from what I did the first. This is an old trick to play on a pathologist and the clinician is very pleased when he trips him up in this way.

There was once a famous pathologist who described a special kind of rare tumor of bone that usually occurs in children. The chief point about this tumor was that it looked vicious but really wasn't. It came to be known by the pathologist's name, let us say "Jones's tumor." Every time another pathologist came across a bone growth that seemed to fit into the category of a Jones's tumor he would send Dr. Jones his slide and the answer invariably came back that it wasn't the same thing at all. Finally one exasperated pathologist asked Dr. Jones for a sample of a true Jones's tumor that he might keep for reference. Dr. Jones obliged. Months later the pathologist changed the label on Dr. Jones's own slide and sent it back to Dr. Jones as an unknown one for his interpretation. The answer still came back, "This is not a real Jones's tumor." So you can see that surgical pathology has its limitations and the practicing surgeon ought to know what they are. He sometimes doesn't.

9

My Critical Friends
the Internists

A L T H O U G H the developments of modern surgery have brought us pathologists into almost daily contact with surgeons, we have a much older and, on the whole, more intimate relationship with the doctors on the general medical service of the hospital—doctors who are known as internists or, in the somewhat broader term, as clinicians. In the hospital they treat patients with major internal diseases and are not ordinarily concerned with minor ailments or with those that fall into the domain of other specialists. Their activities are, therefore, much more restricted than are those of the so-called general practitioner. Doctors in private practice who treat only the major internal diseases are also known as internists. Actually, the dividing line between a general practitioner and an internist is not always too clearly defined. The practice of the pure internist is largely as a consultant called in by other doctors. The young doctor who sets out to be an internist often has a difficult row to hoe before he attains bona-fide status as one, and in his early years of practice, he may be only barely distinguishable from the general practitioner.

The close association between pathologists and internists has a long history. As I have said, the first pathologists were merely medical men who did autopsies as a side line. In the Bellevue archives there are old ledger-type notebooks in which autopsy descriptions are written out in long hand with signatures of famous clinicians of the latter part of the nineteenth century appended. Not until the time of William Welch was the first separate department of pathology formed. And even after pathology had become recognized as a specialty, the liaison with internists remained very close for many years. They continued to be greatly interested in autopsies, and it was considered good practice for anyone intending to specialize in medicine to spend a year or two in pathology. The original membership lists of the New York Pathological Society, the second oldest of its kind (Dublin's is more ancient), consisted largely of practicing clinicians, and there are still a few die-hard clinicians who are members.

Some of the famous doctors of the twenties and thirties began their careers as full-time pathologists and switched to medical practice only many years later.

These doctors never completely lost their interest in pathology. Even after they became successful practitioners they often reminisced fondly of their days as pathologists. They frequently urged young graduates who planned to become internists to first spend a year in pathology. Even now there are many medical internships which include several months of assignment to pathology.

Nevertheless, something of a schism has gradually developed between these two branches of medicine. Many clinicians feel that it is more advisable for a young trainee to spend a year doing research in physiology, chemistry or one of the other so-called basic sciences of medicine. I happen to agree with them to a certain extent, but for reasons very different from their own. Clinicians with a smattering of pathological training can be responsible for the dissemination of slightly inaccurate information about pathological processes. Still, the old tradition that links pathology and internal medicine has deep roots.

The internist's major and most challenging function is that of a diagnostician. When presented with a patient whose illness is obscure, he has to assemble a wide variety of clinical and laboratory data and from them try to resolve the nature of the disease process involved. As any illness progresses, more and more data become available and the chances of finding the right answer usually improve. With the armamentarium of diagnostic aids available today, the clinician's diagnoses are accurate more often than not, but he is still occasionally in for some surprises if the patient dies and is examined at autopsy. He may have spotted the major disease process, but these days old people seldom die of one single uncomplicated disease. They usually have lesser afflictions that may make the clinical history very confusing.

Extraordinary advances have been made in the accuracy of clinical diagnosis during the past two or three decades, and rapid progress is still being made as new diagnostic tests are devised. The average third-year medical student can make correct diagnoses today that even the greatest medical savants could not achieve thirty years ago. I can remember the time when it was considered quite an accomplishment to make the diagnosis of cancer of the lung in a living patient.

One of the differences between an exceptionally talented doctor and an ordinary one is the ease and speed with which he discovers what ails his patients. The ordinary one may eventually arrive at the correct diagnosis, but he requires a battery of tests and may have to observe the patient for prolonged periods before he sees the light. And it is not the final diagnosis that always tells the tale of how successfully a patient was treated, but the impressions formed on admission to the hospital and during the progress of the disease. Reading a clinical chart requires a special technique of its own, and long experience has made me reasonably adept at it. I am chary of attending physicians who write page after page of long progress notes but seldom commit themselves as to what is actually wrong with the patient. It is nice to know all about the patient's blood electrolytes and what heroic steps are being made to keep them in balance, but it is even nicer to know what made them misbehave in the first place.

It is just this remarkable improvement in diagnostic skill that has taken away most of the dramatic appeal of autopsies. Furthermore, the diagnosis is nowadays frequently confirmed early in the illness by examination of suitable bits of tissue that the surgeon has removed. In many instances, autopsy findings have become too strictly anticlimactic to command the attention of attending physicians. As has so often been the case in the history of medical progress, the autopsy-performing pathologists have helped reduce the pertinence of their own services. It is one thing to look for answers at the end of the book if you are pretty sure you are right, and quite another if the problem has baffled you.

On the rare occasions when the autopsy reveals that the internists were not on the right track or missed something really important, a sticky atmosphere is likely to prevail in the autopsy room. In the heyday of autopsies, such disclosures did not dismay; they merely stimulated the clinicians to improve their methods of diagnosis. Nowadays a visit to the autopsy room by the clinicians is likely not to be too rewarding if the pathologist merely confirms what they already know. Or the visit may be embarrassing if something unexpected turns up.

It would be a gross exaggeration to contend that constant attendance at autopsies by clinicians is required if they are to maintain high standards of diagnostic and therapeutic skill. Medical science has developed to the point where the pathological findings can, if the clinician is so minded, receive only superficial attention. For example, the diagnosis of a heart attack can often be made accurately by doctors studying electrocardiographic tracings taken by trained nonmedical personnel who may not ever have seen a human heart. The pioneer cardiologists had to spend much time and effort correlating the structural changes in the heart with the tracings on these records, but now young cardiologists can learn how to interpret them without having recourse to the organ itself. One of the most renowned clinical diagnosticians of recent times had a poor opinion of the value of autopsies and seldom visited the autopsy room in his later years.

All the same, I find it disturbing that there are many heart, kidney and other kinds of specialists who have, since they were second-year medical students, seldom laid eyes on the organs they talk about all the time. When such a cardiologist looks at a patient who has just had a heart attack, he probably does not envision a heart with a damaged area in it; he sees it as a wiggly line on an electrocardiographic tracing. I suppose that this is only to be expected in these days of intensive specialization in all fields. I am told that there are even artists who never go near art museums. In fact, if you should visit the Metropolitan Museum and should happen to observe a rather corpulent and sinister-looking figure examining the works of modern sculpture intensely, it will probably be me, not some artist. I am fascinated by the striking resemblance between modern sculpture and so-called staghorn kidney stones. There is one statue in the museum called "Mother Love," which is an exact replica of one of the more impressive kidney stones in my collection. I get great satisfaction in comparing these two beautiful works of art.

The interest of surgeons in autopsies has never been as keen as that of clinicians. Autopsy-percentage rates on surgical services are usually but not always lower than on medical ones. The chief reason for this is that in many of his patients the surgeon has already had a pretty good look at the diseased tissue during the course of his operative procedure. Furthermore, as I pointed out in an earlier chapter, relatives of patients who have died after an operation are sometimes not disposed to agree to an autopsy. They may say, "You have already performed an operation. Why do you want to do another one?" The surgeon's interest in autopsies is chiefly to check up on the effectiveness of his operative procedures.

I have mixed feelings about clinicians who have had some training in pathology early in their careers and as a consequence sometimes seem to feel that they know almost as much about pathology as any pathologist who devotes full time to it. I firmly believe that such training is useful to them, as it is to surgeons, in helping them to become better doctors. It also keeps alive an interest in pathology, which pathologists appreciate. But when they challenge my position as the infallible dispenser of the last word, I am vexed. There is only one Allah and I am his pathological prophet.

Sometimes such an amateur-pathologist type of clinician informs me that he has examined our microscopic slides and has arrived at an interpretation different from my own. Or he will merely ask me to look at the slides again, implying, whether he does so intentionally or not, that I am such a careless and irresponsible person that I make pathological diagnoses very casually. Then he goes away saying to himself that I am a terrible-tempered character. In all fairness, I should admit that this seldom happens and that the clinicians generally use a more gracious approach when they inquire personally about pathological reports. At least after their first visit to the laboratory.

I can also become vexed at the "little knowledge is a dangerous thing" type of clinician-pathologist who teaches the medical students in their third and fourth years a brand of pathology that doesn't quite jibe with what was taught in the official course on the subject. The specialist who is an expert on the disease of a single organ, the heart, lungs or kidneys, is usually the greatest offender. He has read a great deal on his own particular subject, no doubt much more than the general pathologist has. He thus acquires a great deal of book learning about the pathology of his own specialty. Unfortunately, it is as difficult to learn pathology from a book as it is to learn to play the piano by reading an article on piano playing. Thus when such a doctor says that any specialist knows more about the pathology of his own specialty than does the average general pathologist, neither Allah nor I am amused.

These specialists frequently borrow lantern slides of pathological processes to show in their lectures to the students. It is necessary to have such lantern slides clearly labeled; otherwise the specialist might not be able to identify them. I once proved this by playing a trick on a cardiologist friend of mine who had asked for the loan of some lantern slides on rheumatic heart disease. He was scheduled to give a lecture to a sizable group of cardiologists. Now this doctor happens to be an extremely able cardiologist, even if he is not associated with the same medical school as I, but his pretensions to knowledge about the pathology of heart disease are a little absurd. So I labeled a picture of the normal cervix of the uterus as "stenosis of the mitral valve" and included it in the batch of heart slides. A stenotic heart valve is one that is thickened, rigid and narrowed, as is the cervix. In fact, the cervix looks like a more exquisite stenosis than any diseased heart valve ever could. The joke misfired. Not only was the lecturer unaware of the substitution, but several members of the audience complimented him on the excellence of his illustrations. And I did not have the courage to tell him of the fraud. A thing like that can get you unfrocked.

Even though some clinicians no longer have an absorbing interest in autopsies, they are without exception in favor of maintaining a high autopsy-percentage rate on their services. (This rate is calculated very simply from the total number of deaths that occur on a hospital service and the number that are examined at post-mortem.) There are several reasons for the clinicians' concern, the most important of which is that they know the hospitals with the best reputations almost without exception have relatively high autopsy-percentage rates. The corollary almost invariably follows. Furthermore, hospitals must maintain fairly high autopsy rates in order to be approved for intern and resident training.

The autopsy-percentage rates of all approved hospitals have, in recent years, been published annually as part of a large tabulation of hospital statistics in the *Journal* of the American Medical Association. This is done primarily for the benefit of medical-school graduating classes seeking information about hospitals that offer house-staff appointments. The figure is one of the few statistics that give any information about the comparative status and quality of different hospitals, although it is, of course, a most imperfect evaluation of their relative merits.

It is curious that the annual lists of autopsy rates as a whole show a gradual tendency to rise in the majority of hospitals. This, I think, is due to the increased ease with which consent for post-mortem examination can be obtained from relatives of the deceased, and not to any increased zeal on the part of the medical staff in obtaining such permission. Nevertheless, it cannot be denied that the heads of the professional services keep a periodic watch on their own percentage rates and occasionally exhort their staffs to improve them.

The pathologist is himself not primarily responsible

or accountable for the autopsy-percentage rate. Yet when a sharp drop in the percentage is announced at a regular staff meeting, everyone turns around and gives the pathologist a dirty look, as though he has been lying down on the job. I have never enjoyed the luxury of working in a hospital where there was a dearth of autopsies. It only takes about one autopsy a day to keep a pathologist happy and gay. Anything more than that constitutes a surfeit. The great Rokitansky, whose memory I have already sullied, is said to have performed an average of ten autopsies a day during most of his professional career. This no doubt explains the short cuts in technique that he devised.

I am not impressed by high autopsy rates when I suspect that attendance at them by clinicians has been negligible. An autopsy-attendance rate would be a much more valuable guide in indicating how conscientious the doctors of a hospital are in checking on their own diagnostic accuracy. Since I am an ornery individual, I have always instructed my mortuary dieners to keep a record of attendance by clinicians. This is largely for my own edification, but it also helps me determine if the pathology residents are doing their job of demonstrating what they find as expeditiously as possible. When I go through these lists I usually find that, with a few startling exceptions that work both ways, doctors who are a cut above the average in ability and reliability frequent the autopsy room, whereas the really poor ones seldom come at all.

The autopsy room is not the only place where pathologists and clinicians fraternize. We meet periodically in the conference room. There is a time-honored meeting, held at regular intervals in most hospitals, that is called a clinical-pathological conference. The purpose of such meetings is to present for the benefit of the whole staff both the clinical and pathological aspects of unusual or interesting cases. This custom is said to be peculiar to American medicine.

I have no idea how the practice of holding such conferences originated. When I was a student, they were already a well-entrenched procedure. In fact, they were at the peak of their importance. I remember that clinical-pathological conferences were held weekly in the main auditorium and were heavily attended by physicians, residents and students. As interest in autopsies has declined, the audiences have tended to dwindle. To counteract this, the conduct of conferences has frequently been modified to reduce the pathologist's participation and increase the clinician's. I am not complaining about this. The old-fashioned session in which a pathology resident stood up and read a ten-page description of his findings was a great bore.

No two hospitals hold clinical-pathological conferences in exactly the same way, but in general there are two major varieties. In the old-fashioned kind, with which I grew up, the case picked for presentation has come to autopsy recently, so that details are still fresh in the memory of the doctors who treated the patient. The senior attending physician on the ward where the patient died presents the clinical story, explaining how the clinicians had arrived at a diagnosis and why this or that therapy was used. The pathologist then gives his findings and attempts as best he can to correlate the pathological story with the clinical. He sometimes queries the clinicians as to possible explanations for discrepancies between clinical and pathological data.

Obviously this kind of conference is intended for more than instruction. It serves as a check on the quality of medical care the hospital provides, and it works best in small, closely knit institutions where there is a great deal of intimacy between members of the professional staff. Unfortunately, the tendency here is to select for presentation cases in which differences of opinion between clinicians and pathologists might lead to controversy. These meetings do not always work out too happily.

The second major variety of clinical-pathological conference was introduced forty or fifty years ago by a celebrated Boston internist named Cabot, as might be expected. It was first known as a differential-diagnosis clinic. Dr. Cabot, working from a detailed account of the clinical history, would analyze the nature of the illness of some deceased patient. As he went along he would discuss the significance of each feature of the case. Finally he would summarize his interpretation and offer his clinical diagnosis. The pathologist would then state briefly what was actually found at autopsy.

This type of presentation can be an impressive tour de force when done expertly. It is much more difficult to make an accurate diagnosis from such a written account than at the patient's bedside. I once had the opportunity of attending a conference given by Dr. Cabot and was greatly impressed at the skill of his analysis. It had almost an intuitive quality. He was given a case in which the patient had two independent and obscure diseases and he successfully ferreted them both out. These performances became very famous, and Dr. Cabot's discussions were collected and published in several volumes. His type of conference was widely imitated and was often incorporated into the curriculum of medical schools. Students considered the method very instructive. Every medical school has one or more clinicians particularly adept at it.

This approach was soon introduced to the regular clinical-pathological conferences of many hospitals. The principal speaker became not one who had supervised the medical care of the patient under discussion but one who had no personal knowledge of the case prior to conference. As a teaching exercise, these conferences are valuable, but the intent for which they were originally designed has become secondary.

Occasionally it comes to pass that the clinician discussing the case arrives at the correct diagnosis without having built up a strong case to support it. Overt chicanery is seldom involved, however. It is usually a case of memory being better than perception. No attempt is made to conceal the pathological findings at the time of autopsy and the completed pathological report is attached to the clinical record. The clinician may not be conscious that he has heard about the pathological findings, but there is such a thing as a subconscious distant recall. It is the thing that dreams, extrasensory perceptions and thoughts that get stuck at the tip of your tongue are made of.

Pathologists and clinicians meet less formally in the staff dining room. It is here that I sometimes exact a cruel vengeance from clinicians who I feel have been neglecting the autopsy findings of their own cases. "By the way," I say, "we have just reviewed one of your cases and were surprised to find that he had toxaplasmosis." Or perhaps I mention Fiedler's myocarditis or some other such rare condition. This usually arouses a kind of disturbed or incredulous reaction, such as, "Which patient was that?" "Gosh, I just can't remember his name," I say, leaving the doctor with a certain feeling of unfulfillment.

Lest the intent of the foregoing account of how pathologists and clinicians live together within the confines of a hospital be misunderstood, I hasten to set the record straight. I love, honor and—when I am sick— obey implicitly all clinicians. I am fond of them all, regardless of shape, size or condition of relative servitude —even of the dapper ones who sport mustachios with waxed ends, even of the ones who are aggressively lacking in humility.

I have always had a particularly high regard for the proficient general practitioner and for his counterpart in hospital medicine, the chief of the medical service. With the general practitioner I have had only limited contact, but on almost every occasion I have been impressed by his accomplishments. He may know little about gas chromatography, paper electrophoresis or any of the other advanced techniques now in use in research laboratories. In fact, he may in a distant way be closer to the African witch doctor with painted face and feathers sticking out fore and aft than he is to the medical-school savant. I have no doubt that the average witch doctor, after his own fashion, is also an accomplished general practitioner.

The greatest asset of the general practitioner is the quality Osler described as "equanimity." When I was a beginner in medical school, I was advised to read certain classical writings in the medical field. Today's students are urged to keep up with the new marvels of medical discovery by reading the green, blue or yellow medical journals or various others with different-colored covers. Such students soon view as hopelessly outdated and archaic everything written about medicine that is older than five years. I remember trying to read *Religio Medici*, by Sir Thomas Browne, and finding it poetically ponderous and full of noble ideas that I couldn't quite perceive in depth. Sir William Osler's collected essays, called *Equanimitas*, was a very different affair. It was highly readable and inspiring. I have recently reread it and find that it still retains its charm and has not lost too much of its pertinence. I can hope only that it will continue to influence successive generations of doctors.

In the first celebrated essay, Osler pointed out the importance of the doctor's bearing toward his patients and urged all students to strive to attain the state of what he called equanimity. This sounded like admirable advice, although equanimity is a quality somewhat alien to the pathologist. I did not appreciate its significance until later years, when I watched doctors actually handle patients and realized that all good doctors have this quality in large measure and that they acquire it more or less naturally, whether or not they have ever read Osler.

The competent general practitioner is the best tranquilizing pill ever invented. He can go into a house filled with turmoil and distress, and with a few soft words or even none at all, relieve anxiety, reassure relatives, and create an atmosphere of composure. And if it is bad news he has to impart, he can get the unfortunate patient to accept his fate. Often he achieves these things without making an exact diagnosis or prescribing curative medications. It is my belief that this is still a most important accomplishment and that it often transcends scientific erudition. I have seen moving pictures of witch doctors and believe that they sometimes have that certain look on their faces that proclaims them to be authentic practitioners of medicine. I make this comparison without meaning any offense to either group. Quite the contrary.

With chiefs of hospital medical services I have had more enduring exposures. By far the most important figure in any hospital setup is the head of the medical service. A hospital's status rises or falls depending on the qualities of its commanding medical officer. This is because the general medical service he runs should be, and usually is, the dominant service of the hospital. It works up many of the patients admitted to the hospital before they are redistributed to other services, and it is consulted by all the other specialized services.

It has been my good fortune to work in hospitals with a number of chiefs of medicine, all of whom I have regarded with boundless esteem. In them I have recognized that same quality of undisturbable equanimity, which, I have claimed, is one of the general practitioner's chief stocks in trade. In the hospital its uses are much greater, since the head medical man employs it in all his varied and multitudinous dealings. I suspect it is sometimes the responsibilities of the job that make the man, rather than the other way around. In some instances, at least, newly appointed chiefs of medicine seem to develop virtues that no one suspected they possessed when they were junior staff members.

An old-fashioned chief of medical service is likely to be more highly regarded by his pathologist than by the younger members of his own staff. To the medical students he is apt to appear as an old fuddy-duddy who is hopelessly behind the times. Medical students have the unpleasant custom of concocting venomous nicknames for their teachers. My own sobriquet, which I shall not divulge, has always saddened me a little. Custom has long decreed that at least one member of the faculty be dubbed "Cloudy Swelling" or, at the very least, "Shifting Dullness." The names derive from pathological changes that occur in certain diseases. Not infrequently the professor of medicine acquires such dubious distinction.

The junior staff members of a medical department sometimes say that their chief is a figurehead who doesn't do anything. They admit that the service runs well and has good morale, but they attribute the chief's success to his hard-working lieutenants who, they believe, are running the show. Comes the time when the chief retires, and very rapidly the character of the entire service changes. Everyone suddenly realizes that the old man really was the boss who controlled the department, even though his directing activities may have been invisible.

From my own junior days I remember one hoary old medical chief who ran a topnotch service, but was seldom given much credit for it. One day one of his assistant residents, while ensconced in the men's washroom, heard his chief's voice saying, "Howard, how would you like to stay on as senior resident next year?" My friend Howard was highly indignant at this approach. "What a way to run a service," he complained. I think he was particularly incensed by the fact that the old chief's diagnostic acumen was such that he was able to identify sight unseen the occupant of Cubicle 2.

A striking talent of many medical chiefs is the ability to settle arguments or controversies between groups of doctors on his service without rendering any definite opinion of his own. Let us say one group thinks that a certain patient should be operated on immediately and the other does not. The chief is consulted and proceeds to talk all around the subject, discussing the pros and cons and seemingly leaving the decision hanging in midair. Yet before the chief is through, everyone present knows perfectly well whether or not the operation will ever be performed.

On ward rounds a good chief of medicine exhibits a remarkable ability to detect little things that bother a patient, things no one else ever noticed, and to win with a few words the confidence of a difficult patient. He is the kind of gent to whom patients tell things they have concealed from all previous medical questioners. Many a time I have seen the medical chief obtain by a few simple questions information that completely changed the diagnosis and treatment of a patient who presumably had been thoroughly worked up by several members of the house staff. Or he may convert a depressed patient into a cheerful one by some simple maneuver, such as changing the position of the patient's bed on the ward. It may sound as though I were describing the activities of a single accomplished doctor. Actually I am giving a composite picture of several men.

Chiefs of medical services have a role to play and an obligation to live up to the part. The ideal chief should have a gleaming hairless pate, carry a bit of a paunch in front and wear a long white coat that comes down to his ankles. Once upon a time, the importance of a doctor in the hierarchy of a hospital could be told by the length of his white coat. I think it is unfortunate that the coat caste system has passed into oblivion. These days it is difficult for the patient to distinguish the professor from the porters. A resident at Mt. Sinai Hospital once caricatured the situation very deftly in a hospital publication. The full-time full-time doctor was completely enveloped by an enormous white greatcoat; the full-time part-time and the part-time full-time doctors wore less voluminous coats, and so on down the list to the ignominious no-time any-time doctor or the mere hanger-on in the outpatient clinic. The last named, in fact, was naked except for a dickey around his neck. The passing of the coat system may make it hard to place most doctors, but you can always identify the surgeons. These are the fellows who roam around the hospital in those crumpled green scrub-suits with hairy bosoms exposed. Recently I saw one at the hospital lunch counter still wearing his rubber operating gloves to avoid the necessity of rescrubbing his hands when he returned to the operating rooms. You can always depend on the surgeon to attain a new note of elegance.

The abdominal paunch, although not indispensable, is a most helpful attribute to all good heads of medical services, for it is here that the spirit of equanimity finds its best anchorage. Gautama Buddha was not a thin man. It would not have suited his religious principles. I once returned from a meeting of the American Heart Association thinking that never had I seen such a bunch of lean and hungry clinicians whose equanimity was so insecurely anchored. As purveyors of that magic quality, they are in the same position as a bald-headed barber trying to sell hair restorer to a patron who has more hair than himself. These men are the unfortunate victims of their own propaganda. The doctors, these days, try to persuade their heavier patients to lose weight and feel most self-conscious if they themselves are a bit over the line. As a consequence, there is a greater furor about dieting among clinicians than there is among chorus girls or film stars. The reason for this situation is the widely held belief that fat men are more vulnerable to heart attacks than thin ones. This may in fact be the case, but all of us must die sometime, and it is a moot point as to how much we should disrupt our lives or deny ourselves the things that please us in order to delay death. Now that the "old man's friend," pneumonia, has been taken from us almost completely, there are more dreadful ways of dying than from a massive heart attack. At least a heart attack is quick, if painful.

Doctors believe, with reason, that persuading an overweight person to lose weight can do nothing but good, even if they are dubious about preventing heart attacks by this means. But different individuals have different capacities for controlling their appetites, and many of us are not so constituted as to be able to maintain a rigid diet. All the doctor does to this type of person is to cause considerable anxiety and a feeling of guilt. I am personally pessimistic about the idea of controlling arteriosclerosis in man by elective dietary means alone.

The evolutionists tell us that man is descended from the apes, most of whom are natural vegetarians. It is quite possible that man has perverted his natural food habits faster than his stomach has been able to learn to assimilate all the things it is loaded with. The versatility of our mind, creating improved living standards, may have exceeded the versatility of our digestive tract. But it is rather late in the game to turn the clock back. It might be simpler to let the evolutionary process eliminate those who cannot make the proper physiological adaptations. But evolution isn't much aided by diseases that occur relatively late in life.

I think it unfortunate that clinicians have become so involved in their dietary preachments that they have to serve as models in order to be effective persuaders. It is difficult to maintain a high level of equanimity while you are suffering from hunger pains. Doctors owe it to their patients to eat plenty of meat and potatoes. It is traditional that doctors make such sacrifices.

10

My Bitter Enemies
the Residents

I T I S nearly 5 o'clock in the afternoon and the telephone rings again. The pathologist's telephone always rings incessantly. I answer it and it is one of the more intrepid residents, young Dr. Kildare. He has a fine capacity for indignation and he is making the most of it.

"I must say this is a fine state of affairs. *Your* laboratory has just refused to do an emergency serum bilirhubarb."

"But serum bilirhubarbs are not on the list of acceptable emergency laboratory tests," I reply.

"I can't help that. I must have it done immediately."

"Would you mind explaining to me just why you need it this evening?"

"That is my decision to make. I am in charge of the patient and I can order anything I think necessary. I must have it, must have it, simply must have it."

"Don't you realize that you are causing us considerable inconvenience and that the regular night technician cannot do this complicated test? One of the daytime technicians will have to stay overtime to do it."

"Doctor," he says, reaching a new level of indignation, "I have taken the Hippocratic oath and you are not going to prevent me from living up to it."

And so with much grumbling on my part, and even more grumbling from the technician who has to stay after hours, the test is done. The next day I have a highly agitated technician on my hands.

She says, "I couldn't reach Dr. Kildare to report the results of the emergency serum bilirhubarb last night. The nurse said he left the hospital five minutes after he ordered the test because he suddenly remembered he had an early dinner engagement."

"What about the other doctors on the ward?"

"No one else knew anything about the emergency serum bilirhubarb."

"What happened to the critically sick patient?"

"We finally located him in the patients' dining room. He was having himself a couple of fast hot dogs."

And so goes my day. It is now after 5 and all the secretaries and technicians have departed but the phone continues to ring. This time it is a surgical resident whom I don't even know and who obviously doesn't know me. He doesn't even sound like a doctor. I wonder if it is another patient or relative calling up to get restricted information, a thing that sometimes happens. He wants to know the result of a biopsy examination on a patient named John Smith. I ask him to wait until the next day and to call during regular hours but he insists that he must know immediately because the patient is scheduled for operation the next morning at 8 o'clock.

I unlock doors and filing cabinets and finally discover that biopsies on three patients named John Smith have been examined in the past few days and the reports on all have long since been sent to the wards.

"Which particular John Smith did you have in mind?" I ask.

"I just want to know about the John Smith I am going to operate on."

"Do you know his hospital registration number?"

"I've got more important things to do than memorize registration numbers," he replies acidly.

"Why don't you look at the pathological report on the chart?"

"Look, all I want to know is the diagnosis. Why are you giving me such a hard time?"

By this time it occurs to me that he is not calling from the hospital at all, but has had sudden second thoughts about the operation he is to perform and realizes that he has never looked at the pathological report. He probably doesn't want to call the ward directly because he knows it will sound peculiar to ask for such information at this late date.

I say, "Do you consider it good practice to take out a

patient's lung on the basis of a telephone conversation with someone you don't know and who isn't even sure what patient you have in mind?"

"Now see here, Doctor," he replies angrily, "I took the oath of Hippocrates and neither you nor anyone else is going to stop me from doing my duty."

It is about 12 o'clock when I get home after spending the evening with friends, and as I unlock the front door I hear the telephone ringing furiously. It is an operating-room aide at the hospital. He tells me that Dr. Jones, a surgical resident, is performing an emergency appendectomy and has found a tumor in the appendix known as a carcinoid. I tell him to extend my tenderest felicitations to Dr. Jones and to inform him that I will drink a toast to the occasion and break the glass in the fireplace.

"But he wants you to come in and do a frozen section."

"Ask him why," I reply.

Pretty soon he comes back to the telephone and says, "Dr. Jones thinks you have to do frozen sections on all tumors and there doesn't have to be a reason."

"I know, I know," I say wearily. "Ask him if he ever took the Hippocratic oath."

Residents, I love thee not. These stories are of course a parody of actual incidents, but not too much of a parody. The resident's interpretation of the Hippocratic oath is as follows: "Nothing is too good for the patient, provided it doesn't involve any extra effort on my own part."

159

The grievance committee of the Society for the Prevention of Cruelty to Interns and Residents is therefore advised to remain on the alert. No doubt its radar warning system is already sounding off loudly. For I am about to commit the sacrilege of sacrileges by discussing these noble, self-sacrificing members of the medical profession as though they were ordinary, if slightly immature, people. This will probably come as a great shock not only to all interns and residents but to sentimental editorial and feature writers for magazines and newspapers and to novelists and playwrights who have romanticized these medical men to the point where they have been bewitched by their own good notices.

There may have been a time when interns and residents were dedicated young doctors, full of nothing but the noblest ideals, who were abused and exploited. Those days are long since over. The present crop is in a position to bargain over its services and doesn't hesitate to do so. Their pay, while still modest, is very substantial compared to what it was twenty-five years ago. In terms of percentage it has increased well beyond that of any other medical group. I can make this extravagant statement without looking up the figures, because in depression years many interns weren't paid at all. They received only room, board and laundry.

I do not contend that there has been a sudden deterioration in the moral fiber of medical-school graduates. It is just that the law of supply and demand operates in this sphere the same way it does in all other forms of human endeavor. The marked increase in the number of hospital admissions and the expansion of hospital-bed facilities have created a greater demand for interns and residents than can be completely satisfied. The same holds true for nurses. There is a constant hue and cry about the shortage of the latter, but only recently has there been much public discussion of the hospital house-staff problem.

Nurse's aides or so-called practical nurses now perform a large portion of what used to be the nurse's job. It would be interesting to see statistics on the number of registered nurses who accept desk jobs in large commercial quasi-medical enterprises, such as industrial plants, transportation services, schools and the like, now that all sorts of new opportunities have become available to them. The shortage is chiefly of bedside nurses. To a considerably lesser extent, new opportunities are now available to medical-school graduates, especially in the form of research fellowships. This reduces the number willing to work with sick patients on the wards. Because such a situation prevails, interns and residents can demand special working conditions that exempt them from many of the menial and unpleasant chores that were once an important part of their jobs.

What used to be the traditional duties of interns and residents—drawing blood samples; doing blood counts, urinalyses, and blood-group typing; taking X-rays and performing after-hour emergency laboratory tests, and other menial and distasteful chores, including service as glorified messengers—have been transferred to technicians, ward clerks and other nonprofessional help.

Much of the increased cost of medical care can be attributed to the need for extra paid personnel to perform the tasks once done practically gratis by residents and interns.

I do not begrudge them their hard-won liberation from such belittling duties or their increases in pay. What with fellowships, training grants, special financial inducements to enter government medical services, and part-time outside jobs that they never would have been able to carry in the old days, many residents now make from five to ten thousand dollars a year. What I do resent is their attitude that they are still the same downtrodden, self-sacrificing and overworked group they were twenty-five years ago. Except for the occasional night or weekend tour of duty, they have become largely nine-to-five boys on a five-day-week schedule.

The evolution of a doctor from premedical student to adult stage requires as many metamorphoses as does the development of an amphibian. The most drastic transformation occurs between the time of graduation and the completion of residency training. It is in this period that the student is rapidly converted into a doctor. Fortunately it is only a brief period in the entire span of a medical career. Unluckily for me, I am constantly exposed to and bruised by successive batches of raw recruits, each repeating the same mistakes and making the same unreasonable demands as the predecessors. Unluckily for me, I have to deal constantly with residents who are not under my supervision and are not beholden to me in any way, and since I lack persuasive charm, I can control some of them only with a sharp tongue and a short temper. Perhaps my affection and sympathy for head nurses derive from the fact that they are in the same boat. In fact, they take a much greater beating. On the other hand, they can form romantic or motherly attachments to the rascals and not mind the shoving around so much.

The transformation of a resident into a full-fledged doctor involves as profound an alteration as the tadpole's when, in an agony of physiological adaptation, it sheds its formidable tail and aerates its lungs. Except that the tadpole has the decency to retire to a convenient edge of the pool and perform in private. The resident requires the parturitional services of staff physicians, nurses and the nonvoting member of the triad; namely, the patient.

In the days of yore, the boys in white knew quite well that they were being given a precious and vital opportunity to learn how to be doctors. Their menial chores and duties served in lieu of tuition fees. They received more individual instruction than they did when they were students and had to pay for it. Students have almost as much right to be paid as interns, and I am not opposed to that either, but the present-day resident assumes that he is entitled to a very formal and thorough training program and that his obligation to give services in return is more or less optional. In the handling of patients he may insist on considerable latitude without interference from senior staff personnel. He will very likely gripe against labeling specimen tubes, charting laboratory results, filling out requisition forms or even checking the caution tags on blood-transfusion bags as beneath his dignity, yet he knows that such important if petty tasks ought not to be entrusted to nonprofessional help. When my ten-thousand-a-year trainee calls up and says he won't be in today because his wife wants to go shopping and he has to stay home with the baby, I say there ought to be a law, especially when he acts as though it was mighty white of him to call up and announce his intentions at all.

Where does the ward patient fit into this deal? He is the passive recipient of all the residents' favors. When such patients received medical care free of charge, it was reasonable for them to expect some inconvenience, such as serving as demonstration models for students and interns. Now that many of them pay substantial amounts for their medical care, either directly or through hospital insurance, they too have a right to feel they are making a sizable donation to the interns' and residents' education. My point is that the pittance medical-school graduates used to receive during their postgraduate training period was never intended to be the whole of their compensation, and the services they once rendered made up for the trouble others were put to while they learned their trade properly.

The novice intern or junior resident who has just begun his training in a specialty is closely supervised by his superiors. He is not in a position to do serious injury, yet he can cause considerable discomfort to patients while he acquires experience. He depends more on the help of nurses than he is likely to admit. The head nurse can be the most important person on a ward. From long experience she knows the practical side of handling patients—changing dressings, administering medications and a thousand and one other things. She may have a better idea of the drugs required than does the unpracticed house-staff member, and in the latter's first few days on a service, he is usually grateful for her tactfully offered suggestions.

One of my biggest complaints about interns and residents is that their pride is such, they will seldom admit ignorance and inexperience. They feel that if they have to call on someone else for help, they will lose face. Since only an irresponsible doctor will put his own prestige before that of the patient's welfare, this hardly ever happens, but sometimes he procrastinates just a little before seeking assistance. I have a warm feeling of devotion and of great indebtedness to all the nurses and staff doctors who have taken care of me during my many illnesses. I do not have such a feeling about any of the interns or residents who crossed my path of sickness and there are several whose memory still fills me with loathing. I suspect, though, that they all grew up to be very fine doctors. I just didn't enjoy their left-handed-monkey-wrench way of growing with experience.

I should make it clear that I do not object to the boys in the white suits as persons. It is their transient doctoral pubescence I find annoying, especially when it is complicated by an acneform eruption of complaints. I can hardly wait for some future Dr. Spock to write a book about behavior patterns in growing interns and residents. As bedside visitors when you are a patient, they can be very agreeable. They helped me pass many a long day during my own illnesses and I suppose such visits filled in the blank periods for them between coffee breaks and conferences. I enjoyed listening to them explain for hours on end how busy they were.

Bedside conversations with interns and residents usually run in one of three channels. Either they talk about their ambitious plans for the future, or they discuss their personal problems, or they complain about the obstacles besetting them in their hospital duties. The last subject lies at the core of my disdain for them and I will discuss that later, after I give my version of how the intern-and-resident system of hospital medical care developed.

I am not the kind of person who inspires confidences of a personal nature, but the doctor in the room next to mine when we were both recovering from tuberculosis was an extraordinary confessor type. He ran a very busy, if impromptu, clinic for distressed interns and residents, who consulted him all day long. I practically got to be his secretary. A distressed resident, seeing one of his colleagues deeply embroiled in conversation with this doctor, would stop off in my room and I would say, "Dr. H. is tied up right now. Why don't you come back in about an hour?"

Their confessions to me seldom went deeper than admitting that they should not have listened to their par-

ents but gone into archeology or literature or some other
career they once fancied. I could sympathize with their
temporary rebellion against the yoke of a life limited to
sick and demanding people. Not the smallest part of an
intern's training is learning how to wear this harness,
which will be with him henceforth. It is not one I was
ever able to adjust to gracefully and this probably
explains in part why I became a pathologist. I prefer
patients who have passed beyond the complaining
stage but I can make obeisance to those who carry this
not inconsiderable burden as a permanent fixture in
their lives.

Interns' conversations with me were likely to take on
the aspect of formalized daydreaming or wish fulfillment. They would talk to me by the hour about the fan-
ciful and impractical research projects they hoped to
carry out someday. The considered me a suitable audience, not because they mistook me for some big research
luminary, but simply because I represented a segment of the medical profession that is not tied down by
the care of patients. These interns were often poorly
adjusted and misplaced as far as their ward work
was concerned. They were apt to be forgetful and un-
realistic about their routine obligations. They were the
ones who invariably had a large pile of unfinished clinical summaries to complete.

I remember one in particular whose head was always
in the clouds. One day he had to take me to the X-ray
department for a special kind of examination known
as a tomagram. He had to fill out a requisition slip for

the test and so he started to ask me questions. "When were you born?" he asked, and I said, "1848." He wrote that down without hesitation. "How much do you weigh?" he asked, and I said, "Three hundred and fifty pounds," and he wrote that down. (I don't weigh an ounce more than two hundred.) "What is your race?" I replied, "Chinese," and, by golly, he wrote that down. By this time I had decided that he knew he was being ribbed and was playing along deadpan. But as he wheeled me along the corridor to the elevator, I could see he was mulling the whole thing over in his mind. Finally he asked me, somewhat incredulously, "Are you really Chinese?" I hope for his sake he has found his way into the research laboratories.

Perhaps I should start at the very beginning and explain how interns and residents are selected, what their functions are, and how this bizarre system of hospital medical care came into existence. First of all, the terminology should be straightened out. "House staff" is a term applied to both interns and residents, and derives from the days when all such doctors were expected to live in the hospital and be available for off-hour duty. Nowadays the majority are married and live out of the hospital, but they are still scheduled for nighttime and weekend call. Many hospitals now have special overnight quarters for the doctors on call. Interns are doctors who are spending their first year after graduation as a member of the house staff. During this year, they are supposed to acquire general knowledge of a broad field, such as medicine or surgery. Residents are doctors who have completed their internships and are specializing in some particular field of medicine. To complete the requirements for specialization, they will have to spend at least three to four years as a resident. Interns are no longer necessarily "interned" in the hospital, and residents seldom "reside" in it, but the old terms linger on.

Up to about the time of the First World War the bulk of medical practice took place in the home or in the doctor's office. Many medical-school graduates went directly into practice without spending any time in the hospital, or became assistants to practicing doctors. If they wanted to specialize they went abroad or served on a hospital staff, but the requirements for specialization were very elastic. House staffs at that time were most meager. Often they consisted of a single chief resident and a handful of interns. The chief resident's job was often a fairly permanent one, and he occupied a position of great authority in the hospital since he was usually the only trained doctor available at all times. He was often a graybeard. The interns merely assisted him and were largely trained by him.

During the period between the two world wars, the internship system was greatly expanded, chiefly because hospital care became an ever-increasing feature of medical practice, but there was only a slight increase in resident staffs. Many hospitals offered what was known as a two-year rotating internship and this was greatly in demand by the graduating class of medical students. During this two-year period an intern rotated from service to service, usually spending about four months on each one, and when he completed his tour, he was supposed to have received a broad enough training in all fields to be able to go into general practice. The "specialty" services, such as orthopedics, pediatrics, neurology, and the like, had no house staff of their own or at most a single resident. The needs of these services were met by the rotation of interns.

In this era the total number of internships available was less than the total number of graduates and it was harder to get a desirable internship than to get into medical school in the first place. In many hospitals, all that the interns got for their services was room and board and maybe twenty-five dollars a month. Only the extremely undesirable internships paid much more than that. It was recognized that this was a period of training rather than of medical services rendered. One heard far less about underpaid house staffs in those days than one does now.

Interns once worked like dogs, never thought of objecting to menial chores and did little complaining. They were overjoyed just to get a good internship, and were sometimes dropped by the hospital for minor breaches in discipline that today would hardly call for censure. When they were on night call they took it for granted that they might be up all night. Today's interns would scoff at the idea of doing the things their predecessors took as a matter of course. Many an aspiring intern put off marriage because many hospitals refused to accept married interns, on the grounds that they might want an occasional evening off and that they would not be able to concentrate completely on their hospital job. Interns in the old days frequently grew lean and haggard and sometimes worked their way into the t.b. wards as patients. But when they got through these rugged ordeals, they were real doctors prepared to meet any medical situation. I think they learned about as much in those two strenuous years as some of our pampered residents now do in five.

In the late thirties "specialty boards" under the auspices of national medical societies were set up. Their purpose was to prevent unqualified doctors from claiming to be specialists, and to set up minimum requirements for each specialty. In order to be approved as a specialist in any field, the candidate first had to show that he had met these requirements and then had to pass a qualifying examination. For a number of years the specialty boards languished. There was and is, in fact, no law that gave them the right to decide who shall and who shall not be a specialist. During the Second World War, however, the armed forces used specialty-board certification as a simple, standardized means of classifying specialists, and this gave a great incentive to doctors to acquire such certification. Since then, almost every medical-school graduate plans his residency training toward obtaining specialty-board approval in the field of his choice. He no longer wants to waste a second year as an intern, because it will not count as a qualifying year. This has caused a marked reorientation and realignment of house-staff appointments. The residency programs of almost every service have been greatly expanded and residents outnumber interns two or three to one.

In addition, the nature of intern training has changed greatly, as have the types of internships that are sought after. Almost all internships have been reduced to one-year periods instead of the former two. This, in itself, has almost doubled the number of internships available to each year's graduates. Formerly only about half the total number of two-year internship positions became vacant each year. Now most of them do. In the past few years there have been many more internships available than candidates to fill them, a direct turnabout of what used to prevail. The internship lists show no great increase in total number of internship positions; it is just that the turnover is twice as fast. Or, in other words, second-year interns are now called residents. The great increase in house-staff size that shows up in tabulations is in the number of residents. I mention this because when nonteaching hospitals complain that teaching hospitals are taking more house-staff members than before, and more than they need, the teaching hospitals reply that they have the same number of interns they always had.

At the same time there has been a marked change in the kind of internship that the medical-school graduate applies for. Formerly he wanted to get away from the medical-school atmosphere as quickly as he could and work in a hospital where he would have a position of some authority and responsibility, without too many

superiors over him. Today he realizes that he will floun-
der along and keep repeating the same mistakes unless
there is someone to guide him. Therefore he wants the
kind of instruction that teaching hospitals provide. He
also intends to go on to specialty training as a resident
and knows that he can achieve this more easily if he
sticks to a teaching hospital. As a result of all this, only
the good teaching hospitals now fill their internship
quotas, and many hospitals that formerly filled their
staffs without much difficulty may get only a few intern applicants. The hospitals that are considered desirable for internship find it difficult to resist the tempta-
tion and pressures to take more interns than they really
need, and some have greatly increased their intern staffs,
thus further decreasing the availability of interns to
nonteaching hospitals. When I was an intern in the
early thirties, my hospital had a total house staff of
about seventy-five. Today the same institution, with
hardly any increase in bed capacity, has a house staff
of about two hundred.

The net result of all this expansion and shifting
around has led to profound changes in postgraduate
medical education, some good and some not so good.
The hospitals that can't get any house staff are, of
course, severely handicapped. On the other hand, it cannot be denied that an intern has better opportunities for
learning and getting ahead in a teaching hospital than
in a nonteaching one. The only difficulty is that in
hospitals with heavy house staffs, each resident gets to
see relatively few patients, at least in comparison to

the old days. Internships and residencies become an extension of the student curriculum and not, as they should be, a period of furious learning by trial, error, constant repetition and practical experience gained at the bedside.

So now you know what little residents are made of and why I was not enamored of them as a patient. I will now proceed to explain why, as a pathologist, I pluck no daisies in their honor. Students at the end of their fourth year in medical school are as full of book learning as they will ever be during their entire medical career. In addition, they have learned the lingo and may sound like full-fledged doctors. At seminars that I hold regularly to keep my residents up to date with new developments in medicine, the elective students who attend always shine. We call on them when we need some bit of theory explained and they invariably rise to the occasion. They make me realize that the few remnants of basic theory I still remember from my own student days are now pretty much passé and that a brand-new terminology has taken their place. If I had to take the examinations students take, I would flunk them all, except probably the one in pathology, and the only reason I might pass it is that very likely I would be the one who made it up.

After graduation, however, the average student quickly learns that it is not easy to apply his knowledge to the everyday problems he faces as an intern. Much of what he has learned seems superfluous, some of it even misleading. His greatest fear is that the patients will recognize him as a novice and reject his attentions, but he soon learns that the patients do not often question his ability and this gives him confidence. He may soon persuade himself that he is a competent doctor, but nevertheless, beneath his newly acquired surface poise there is often a feeling of insecurity and inadequacy.

In his dealings with the pathologist his thin veneer of self-confidence is sometimes punctured. We can easily see through his pretensions to a competence he has not yet fully achieved and we sometimes expose his petty blunders. These are due mostly to ignorance, and tend to diminish as the intern acquires experience. The deadliest insult you can hurl at a resident is to call him an intern. It is one that I have used effectively on many occasions. The reason for this is obvious. You are telling the resident he still appears to be a beginner.

The most common psychological reaction of insecure house-staff members is to bolster their egos by laying down a barrage of complaints. They complain about the lack of adequate or well-organized instruction, about having to do too much "scut work"—tedious, unrewarding jobs—about not having enough time to read, and about faulty equipment (which usually takes a beating in their inexperienced hands). According to them, not enough outside lecturers are brought in, the X-ray department doesn't cooperate and their important films can never be located (usually after some intern has misplaced them), the administration is inept and hostile, and, most of all, you just can't trust the results of the laboratory.

When I was first placed in charge of a hospital laboratory, I was very much upset by the torrent of complaints that were leveled against the service, and I have never learned to live with it comfortably. My predecessor, however, reassured and enlightened me by explaining its genesis. According to him, the time to start worrying is when the complaining stops, because it means you are probably not fulfilling your function as a pathologist in uncovering the omissions and errors of the clinical staff.

Most of the complaints reach the laboratory second hand. The residents seldom offer documentary evidence of gross errors, preferring to make their charges in a broad, shotgun manner. It is such a convention among residents to vilify the laboratory and impugn the honesty of its technical staff that if you attempt to defend it, they are outraged. Since it is easier to come to the defense of someone other than yourself, I make a practice of saying nice things about the radiological service and it reciprocates. If I say to interns that the radiologists turn out the best X-ray films I have ever seen (it happens to be true in my present post), they look at me as though I had committed an unforgivable breach of etiquette. Recently I sat at the same dining-room table with some interns who were complaining about the inaccuracy of temperature charts that nurses plot in the clinical records. I mention this because it illustrates the rich versatility and painstaking devotion they bring to their criticizing activities. When I suggested that the temperature records were probably more accurate than the blood-pressure readings (which the interns take), they were incensed.

After many years of contemplating this peculiar residential attitude, I have devised a method for scoring interns and residents on what I call the Complaint Index. I believe this index could be widely applied to many nonmedical fields and might take its place among Bernoulli's Principle, the Donnan Equilibrium, the Quantum Theory and even Parkinson's Law in clarifying the motivations of mankind. This index is calculated by dividing the number of complaints made by any one person during a fixed period of time by the number of nice things he says about others minus self-compliments. A score of infinity is considered below average and is very prevalent among interns and residents. As the result of long and exhaustive research I have come to this inescapable conclusion: the poorer the resident the louder and more numerous his complaints.

No one will deny that the results reported by the laboratory are sometimes inaccurate. The laboratory of any large active hospital performs over a thousand tests a day. It would be remarkable if some errors did not occur. But as a rule the technicians who perform the tests are amazingly conscientious. They do not deliberately cheat, as the residents sometimes imply. All sorts of checks are introduced into their procedures to see that their reagents and apparatuses are functioning properly. The most common causes of errors are improperly cleaned glassware, deterioration of stock reagents and the breakdown of mechanical devices. In my own laboratory, most errors come from the mislabeling of specimen containers. If a blood sample has the wrong patient's name on it, the result is bound to be wrong. To me the amazing thing is that, day in and day out, the vast bulk of laboratory results turns out to be as accurate as it is.

The inflation in the number of laboratory tests ordered on hospital patients during the past twenty years makes all other inflations seem like small-time stuff to the pathologist. This is no spiral ascent, but a straight-line rocket into outer space. What makes this possible is that almost all hospital patients carry some kind of insurance that provides for an unlimited amount of laboratory work. If the patients had to pay for the tests out of their own pockets, a rapid deflation would set in. In hospitals where pathologists receive a percentage of gross laboratory income over and above their base salary, the pathologists are very enthusiastic about endless, pointless laboratory tests. But in large voluntary hospitals and in government institutions, the pathologist does not get in on the gravy and takes a mighty dim view of this kind of medical boondoggling.

The device of ordering endless, pointless laboratory tests is used by the resident to camouflage his own inadequacies. First of all, he believes that by ordering everything he can think of, he can create the impression that he is most meticulous and painstaking in his work. If by any chance he has misinterpreted the nature of his patient's illness, his random, shotgun requests for laboratory tests may uncover his error. The clinical pathologist lives in an atmosphere of ever-increasing laboratory work, and he can do little about it because he is seldom in a position to tell whether the tests ordered are really necessary. Meanwhile his budgetary and technical staff requirements expand constantly and he has to struggle with the business administration, who are themselves fighting a sizable deficit, in order to get enough help to keep the laboratory functioning. I haven't the slightest doubt that the cost of hospital care could be drastically reduced without impairing its quality. It might even lead to improvement, because when your laboratory work is done on a mass-production, assembly-line basis, the quality of the work is bound to suffer. I am convinced that the attitude of residents contributes significantly to the rising costs of medical care in hospitals.

When patients' histories are presented at ward rounds and at clinical conferences, the resident starts reading off an endless list of numbers that no one pays much attention to. It sounds as though he were reading a page from the telephone book and sometimes makes just about as much sense. These mysterious numbers are a tabulation of the laboratory data. It is not un-usual to have as many as two hundred laboratory tests recorded in the clinical chart, of which only half a dozen or so have any real pertinence.

The pathologist doesn't get very far when he attempts to remonstrate with the residents. Invariably you get the same answer. "I am here to learn and unless

I can order everything I please, my training as a doctor is being restricted." You try to point out that in most occupations the trainee is taught not to waste materials or make unnecessary manipulations in doing his job, and that the unmistakable sign of the pro in all lines of work is the ability to get things done rapidly and skillfully with the least amount of waste effort and expense. But he will have none of it.

I probably sound like a cantankerous and venomous old crank who has forgotten that he was ever a resident himself. I plead guilty. I have lost touch with the resident's point of view and nowadays all my sympathies are with patients and with the finance department of the hospital. But I can remember that the most exciting and memorable period of my life was the one between my graduation from medical school and the end of my residency. I think that this is probably true for many doctors. In this short period are concentrated the most dramatic incidents of a doctor's career. The entire direction of his future life may be decided, both medically and socially. He will form most of his lifelong friendships, probably get married, decide where he will settle, what branch of medicine he will enter, pick a home and finally an office. Never again will so many things happen to him so quickly.

This was perhaps truer in my day than it is at present. Most of my fellow-residents were unmarried and lived in the hospital, and our life had sort of a monastic element to it. We were poor as church mice and had almost no possessions. The spirit of comradeship and mutual cooperation was unbelievably high when you consider that interns and residents are in a sense competing with each other for advancement. There was little animosity and many strong friendships sprang up almost overnight. We were busy as beavers, completely absorbed in what we were doing, and leading as dedicated a life as it is possible for anyone to have. Many of us found it difficult to take any interest in what happened outside the hospital. We did not have time to think of ourselves or our futures. Perhaps I didn't realize it at the time, but I was as happy and content as I was ever to be again. And besides I was young. We had high-quality bathtub gin that we manufactured ourselves from laboratory alcohol. For relaxation there were squash and tennis courts, not to mention billiard tables. There were never-ending crap games, poker games, and bridge games and, for the more intellectually disposed, even chess. Many of us enjoyed an unusually good rapport with one or more members of the nursing staff. What need did we have of the sordid, mixed-up outside world then in the throes of a dreadful depression? Maybe present-day residents still lead a similar life. If they do, I have little knowledge of it.

When medical students are transformed into housestaff members, a curious shift in "status" often occurs. During their student days some are accepted by their classmates as superior and others as inferior in their abilities. These judgments do not always coincide with those of the faculty. Then there are a large number of students who make no impression on anyone but remain nonentities in the background. When these various groups become interns, surprising developments may occur. Some mousy type may become a pillar of strength overnight, consulted as much by his fellow-interns as they do the senior staff members. Sometimes the latter recognize the value of the formerly mousy one, but more often his prestige remains only with the house staff. Some unimpressive student who barely got through medical school at all suddenly emerges as a "man" in the operating room, an accomplishment that overshadows all his shortcomings.

At the same time certain high-standing students will with equal rapidity recede into the background and become the fifth wheels of the house staff, going through the motions but never making much headway. Their personal charm, flamboyant personalities, glib tongues and ingratiating manner, all of which gave them prominence as students, count for little when they have a clinical diagnostic problem to solve. During residency a man is judged by his true worth more than at any other time in his career.

I would like to be able to report that the new order of "status" established during residency becomes permanent, but unfortunately this is not so. When the residents go forth into practice the old order establishes itself. Student Mouse becomes Doctor Mouse, whereas Resident Mouse becomes Doctor Big Shot with the same facility that he became Student Big Shot. The reader may draw his own moral and conclusions.

11

My Protégés the Students

IF THE morphological pathologist finds himself somewhat in the position of the Ancient Mariner, a microscope slung around his neck instead of an albatross, he at least has one consolation. He enjoys a good rapport with the student body. The medical student approaches the study of disease in a most circumspect sort of way, like a baseball pitcher with an old-fashioned windup. He dissects large frogs, small dogfishes and other species respectively before he gets to medical school, and during his entire first year he picks away at a heavily swathed and pickled cadaver that has only the remotest resemblance to a human being. The peculiar and distinctive odor of the dissecting room permeates him so thoroughly that he is recognized wherever he goes as a first-year medical student. In addition, he is exposed to an overwhelming abundance of more or less abstract theoretical knowledge, only a small fraction of which he absorbs or retains. He is scared to death by this because his classmates pretend to have learned it all and he has to pretend the same. He spends long hours over his textbooks but finds that he cannot focus his attention on what he reads.

The complicated chemical formulas of organic substances elude and haunt him. The distribution of the trigeminal and other cranial nerves is reduced to a mess of untidy and impolite mnemonic jingles. In physiology he gets scratched by indignant cats and becomes quite sick cannulating the arteries of dogs. He has to memorize phrases that mean absolutely nothing to him. "Chronaxy is twice the rheobase" has always haunted me, as has the exact location of Giacomini's band, a strictly nonmusical structure in the brain. In my day, the "specific dynamic action of fats" always used to throw us, although I think this has gone the inevitable way of all complicated medical theories and been replaced by an even more complicated one. The Krebs cycle makes him slightly dizzy. The thirty different and distinct theoretical factors that make blood clot can throw even the most intrepid student for a five-yard loss, and strange enzyme systems with unpronounceable polysyllabic names have him up a tree. "What does all this have to do with medicine?" he says at length to himself. "What made me think I ever wanted to be a doctor?"

So he goes into the second year expecting more of

the same and suddenly finds himself rapt in simple, homely and understandable pathology. He hears about and sees diseased organs, learns about all sorts of maladies and the kind of symptoms that are associated with such diseases. Such a sudden direct exposure to medical problems after his prolonged theoretical hazing in other preclinical courses is an eye opener and makes a profound impression on him. He still hasn't seen any living patients but at least he feels he has made a definite entrance into the real world of medicine, and is grateful and respectful to his pathology instructors for having ushered him into it. As a consequence, in later life the doctor's recollection of his course in pathology often remains more sharply focused in his mind than many other subjects of his early student days. He will frequently tell you that he had an excellent course in pathology, even if you happen to know that he probably had a most indifferent one. The reason he believes this is that it may have been one of the first courses in which studying was not sheer unrewarding drudgery. Sometimes I admit the strong impression made on him was due to his instructor's memorable salty and sarcastic character. Lately, however, we have all become sweet and gentle.

The professor of pathology who taught me as a student was a most extraordinary person who made an indelible impression on me and, in fact, on everyone who came in contact with him. He was a pint-sized type with a highly developed Napoleonic complex who loved to cut big individuals down to his own stature. He had heavy slanting eyebrows that met at mid-line and a penetrating, almost sinister, look that could reduce me instantly to a state of confusion. It had a real hypnotic quality to it, that look. He was also the dean of the medical school, and by the time I came under his instruction, he was more busily occupied with converting a small-time school, housed in a dilapidated old four-story brick building, into one of the leading medical schools in the country than with teaching pathology, but he was still very active in the classroom.

On your very first day in medical school, the dean had a way of greeting you by name and making personal remarks that made you realize he knew all about you. This seemed like an astounding achievement since he had probably seen us only once before, when we applied for admission. Thereafter he seldom addressed you again by your correct name. He had an infallible instinct for finding out which of your classmates you particularly disliked, and he would almost invariably address you by this other fellow's name, a simple way of insulting two people at once. A deadly and slightly humorous sarcasm was his heaviest weapon and he was seldom bested in a verbal duel, largely because he didn't stand on his dignity, as other members of the faculty were accustomed to do. My fellow-students liked to tell tales of "how they told the dean off"—something I never actually saw happen. Most of this was mere wish fulfillment. There was a prevalent belief that the dean liked students who tried to talk back to him, but I don't believe this was true. He preferred the spineless ones

like me. At least he considered me much too defense-
less to pick on while my more obstreperous classmates
took a real beating.

This professor was such an extraordinarily effective
lecturer that he gave "performances" rather than
lectures and made pathology seem very vital and exciting. When he described the struggles of a leucocyte attempting to crawl through a capillary wall to reach
some harmful bacteria, he had us all seated on the edge
of our chairs worrying whether the leucocyte would
make it or not. He could create suspense like Eric
Ambler, and his successive lectures resembled old cliff-
hanger serials of the Pearl White days. Consequently,
pathology seemed a fascinating subject, and it was in
his class that I was overwhelmingly infected by the bug
of wanting to become a pathologist. All the other
courses I took seemed by contrast pallid and inconsequential. I believed that this professor of mine was probably the greatest pathologist in the world, even though
in other ways he was a bit of a stinker. After I got to be
a pathologist, I realized that he wasn't a stinker at all.
He was rather a most dedicated man, who put the interests of the medical school way ahead of his own.
But as a diagnostic pathologist, I regret to say, he was
something less than omniscient, in spite of the profound impression he had made on me as a student.

In his first year the student still retains most of his
boyish undergraduate attitude toward learning. It
clings to him like the aroma of the dissecting room. Between the first and third years a striking development

is apt to take place. The majority of students cease being boys and become more or less self-reliant young men. This sudden growing up can be an astonishing thing. I like to think that the study of pathology has something to do with the sudden maturity, but I admit that around this time the student also attains his chronological majority, and it may be that the change would have taken place anyway. Nevertheless, pathology opens the doors to the world of medicine for him and for this reason, I think, the average student has a high regard for his instructors in this field.

A student's interests can, however, be as mercurial as a mess of polio statistics. As he goes through medical school he realizes that the real white-haired boys of the faculty are the pure researchers, and he becomes fascinated by their various activities. In my day we recognized these types as important but curious eccentrics and never thought of emulating them, probably because research was still considered to be beyond the aspirations of the common man. However, times have changed, and though along about the third year of medical school every ambitious student dreams of becoming a red-hot research man, in most instances, fortunately, he is still practical enough to go on and get his medical degree.

Before he becomes quite that sophisticated, however, a student's main worry is whether or not he will get through medical school at all. During the first two years, few faculty members pay a great deal of attention to the students, who depend largely on their equally ig-

norant classmates for orientation and may arrive at
some pretty bizarre notions of what the score is. They
present a thick protective shell toward the faculty,
but every once in a while, in some informal conversation
with elective students assigned to your department,
you can catch a glimpse of what they think about and
what gross misconceptions they may hold as firm con-
victions. You may try to enlighten them but you may
feel that you are talking about Beethoven to a
rock-'n'-roll enthusiast.

For one thing, the students assume that a large segment of the class will be dropped for poor scholarship.
Many believe that ten per cent of the class is automatically failed each year. On the very first day of
matriculation some old cliché-fancying faculty orator
drags out the old chestnut, "Look at the neighbors on
your left and right. Next year one of you three will be
missing." Actually, not many students are flunked out
of medical school and poor scholarship is not the only
reason for failure. It is the unstable student—the non-
conformist and troublemaker—who often gets sacked.
The average student who keeps his mouth shut and
speaks only when spoken to will get through without
much difficulty. That was the system I used.

Of course, if a student cannot pay his tuition fees he
may get into trouble. Nowadays there are all sorts of
scholarships and part-time jobs that make it possible
to get by even though the tuition fees are formidable.
Many students have nighttime and weekend jobs as
technicians in hospitals, and these can pay surpris-

ingly well. One such part-time-employed student recently turned up in a white Thunderbird, so I suppose things aren't too tough. Perhaps I should give credit to the interns and residents for helping to solve the students' financial problems, since it is because they refuse to do laboratory work that the hospital has to hire students as part-time technicians. If the truth be told, some of these part-time third- and fourth-year students may function during off hours as junior interns in the small hospitals that employ them, and this is not at all to be deplored. They may gain valuable experience in patient care.

If the student can meet his financial obligations, does not insult a professor's wife or expose himself indecently on the front steps of the medical school, his chances of being dropped are not great. I have sat through many faculty meetings that review the grades of students at the end of the year and I know whereof I speak. The meeting begins with the venerable chairman announcing that he will insist on students' being judged entirely on their grades. Anyone who hasn't come up to snuff will be dropped unceremoniously. Everyone present knows that this is mostly hogwash, because the chairman is the biggest softy in the world and hasn't flunked anyone since the Spanish-American War. Actually, out of a student body of a hundred, about fifteen names will appear on the low-grade lists of one or more departments. These cases are discussed individually. Even if the student in question has only one active supporter on the review board, he gets through like a breeze. It is only when he has an active enemy and no supporters that he may be in trouble. Usually after much arguing someone suggests that the student in question be asked to repeat the year. Everyone speedily agrees.

It is true that several students are often flunked at the end of the first year and perhaps two or three at the end of the second, but once over these hurdles they are practically immune. The faculty may later complain that poor students were not dropped at the end of the first year, but they are very loath to fail anyone who has invested two or more years in study, and there are a number of reasons for this reluctance. For one thing, it is recognized that our methods of grading are neither too objective nor too reliable. Years ago the questions we asked on examinations called for lengthy expositions. These were called essay-type questions, and correcting them was a deadly bore. The grader was apt to be very demanding when he read the first few books and graded them severely, but as he went on and saw the same errors repeated over and over again, he became more lenient, especially to students who had the good judgment to write very brief answers. Finally, after he read twenty or so books he became exasperated and started marking strictly again. In other words the grades he gave out depended almost as much on his mood as on the answers.

The difficulty in grading long-answer questions is now recognized, and the short-answer or multiple-choice type have now become the vogue. These can be graded objectively but the nature of medical knowledge is such that, especially when judgment rather than factual knowledge is involved, it is difficult to frame a multiple-choice question in such a way that some valid exception cannot be found. Furthermore, the short-answer questions have become complicated; their answers depend on double negatives canceled out by any number of positive statements, and Part II depends on the answer to Part I. They are more like conundrums or anagrams than legitimate questions. State-board examiners find such complicated questions very effective in weeding out the unqualified graduates of foreign schools who have applied for a medical license. It requires a very intimate knowledge of English to figure out the meaning of some of these intricate short-answer questions. In any case, the students who seem to do particularly well on this kind of examination seldom excel in any other way.

Another reason for not flunking out medical students is that the faculty believes its system of choosing students is so infallible that once they are accepted it is certain they can and will become satisfactory doctors, barring accidents. This is diametrically opposed to the European system, in which almost anyone can enter medical school but the majority never gets through. It is well known that for the past twenty or thirty years college graduates have had great difficulty getting into medical school. Recently this has received much less attention, probably because even high-school graduates in general now have considerable trouble getting into the college of their choice, often regardless of social background. As a matter of fact, there has been some decrease in the volume of medical-schools applications during the past two years, but this may be only temporary, for the Second World War babies now crowding the colleges may shortly enter the contest for medical-school admission.

What is less well known is that in spite of the many medical-school applicants who are rejected, these schools compete vigorously for the more desirable candidates. There probably never have been accurate figures on the percentage of technically eligible candidates who are rejected. A school with an entering class of about a hundred may receive as many as fifteen hundred bona-fide applications. On the face of it, it would appear that only one in fifteen is successful, but most students apply to many schools and the percentage of final rejections is obviously very much lower. It has been claimed that even in the most difficult times one out of every two reasonably well-qualified aspirants got into some medical school, but this figure may have included the ones who had to go to schools in Switzerland, Scotland and other European countries. At the present time it is said that two out of three applicants are accepted.

If the figures are broken down by regions, a very different finding emerges. Many of the Midwestern, Southern and Far Western state medical schools recruit most of their students from their own undergraduate colleges and do not have too many excess applicants. The New York City boy with a degree from a local college has had the greatest difficulty in getting accepted, chiefly because he competes with a large number of applicants with very similar qualifications.

Some of the resourceful maneuvers New York City students have developed in order to beat down the barriers are remarkable. First of all, many of them go abroad to study, even though they know they will have difficulties in obtaining good hospital-staff appointments when they return and will find medical-licensing-board examinations in many states closed to them. All the students enrolled in European schools just prior to the last war were ineligible to obtain licenses in this country. The war was a great break for them—by enlisting in the Medical Corps this barrier could be removed.

Many rejected students once got into medical school by the so-called "back-door" technique. They would enroll as graduate students in some medical-school department with the idea that if they could make an impressive record they could then have their renewed application sponsored and supported by some influential faculty member. This worked in many isolated instances, but it got to be so prevalent that the motives behind such graduate students became increasingly transparent. Now when a student applies for graduate work, the first thing explored is his record of medical-school applications, and a little questioning quickly reveals his ulterior motives.

Premedical students soon learned that it was not at all to their advantage to take the regular prescribed premedical course in college. This immediately identified them with the major group that received almost blanket rejections except for a very few outstanding students. It was wiser to take a general academic course and then pretend that the desire to go to medical school was an afterthought. This removed you just a little bit from the common herd. New York City boys also believed, with less reason, that their chances were much better if they did not have a New York address or if they went to some college far from New York. The main objective, of course, was to dissociate oneself from the pack and try to overcome supposed unfair blanket discrimination in order to be judged on one's own merits.

In spite of the obstacles to medical-school entrance, there can be no question that the brighter and more able as well as the most determined applicants always managed to get in by hook or by crook. I once had a young German-refugee graduate student who was absolutely determined to get into medical school, although he was rejected year after year by almost every school in the country. I was rather fond of him, chiefly because he read Greek poetry for relaxation and was an absolute wizard at chess, though his nervous intensity could be a little disturbing. I exerted what little influence I had on his behalf but it did no good. Because I thought his cause was hopeless and because he looked the type to end up with ulcerative colitis, I did my best to cool his ardor about becoming a doctor but his ambition was absolutely firm. Came the war and the draft and finally the speedup in medical-school curriculums and one day he came into my room triumphantly waving not one but three acceptances from very good medical schools. His only problem was which of the three to accept. I have never seen or heard from him since and I believe he never quite forgave me for trying to dissuade him from continuing his pursuit of a medical career.

Many years ago I served very briefly on the committee that interviewed prospective candidates for admission. It was not a job I relished or was any good at. All the applicants seemed as much alike as peas in a pod. All were rather frightened little boys trying pathetically to make an impression. Generally I could find no valid reason for rejecting or accepting one over any of the others, so I generally marked their application forms as "highly acceptable." This brought about my speedy separation from the committee. The school where I served in this capacity justifiably prided itself on judging its applicants primarily for their scholarship.

A doctor acquaintance of mine, an authentic Princetonian type, once had the idea of starting a school for medical-school rejectees. It was his contention that he could tutor them in such a way that they would invariably make the grade. One of his ideas, I remember, was to dress up the candidate in formal garb including striped pants, a cutaway and an ascot. He thought that a candidate making such a formidable appearance would bowl over his interviewer. He never got around to trying out this Pygmalion experiment but I rather doubt that it would have worked, although the Princetonian himself might have carried it off. As a matter of fact, I strongly suspect he could have got by if he had appeared in moth-eaten bathing trunks, although I, for one, say the hell with *noblesse oblige.*

With so many students trying to pressure their way into medical schools, it is surprising that so little skul-duggery has gone on. One hears about all sorts of in-direct influences that are brought to bear on the dean's office in behalf of certain individuals. Seldom, however, are direct money bribes offered. Occasionally a mis-guided parent will make a substantial donation to a medical school that is raising money, later on acting as though this entitled his son to special consideration when he applies for admission. But I have never heard of an actual instance of successful corruption.

There was once supposed to be a minor politician in Brooklyn who had a nice little medical-school racket going. He persuaded the parents of many medical-school applicants that he had influence in several schools in the metropolitan area. If the parents would give him a thousand dollars in cash, he would undertake to oil the way for their son's acceptance. The money, he said, would be used to pay off the proper medical-school dignitaries. He admitted that he couldn't always guarantee admission but agreed that if he failed he would return the money. As far as anyone knows this politician had no influence in any medical school and never made any attempt to sway any faculty member. He simply pocketed the money and if the student he was supposed to promote got accepted on his own merits, he kept it. If the student was rejected, he simply returned the money. No one could figure out a way of putting this sharpie out of business. The parents of successful applicants were firmly convinced that the thousand-dollar bribe had done the trick, and for all I know this same politician or his successor is still functioning.

In spite of the fact that the majority of applicants are turned away, few medical schools are satisfied that they obtain exactly the caliber of student body they would like. There is no reliable method of comparing the quality of different medical schools, but there can be no question that some are considered much more desirable than others by premedical students. The schools with lesser reputations never cease trying to improve their status and to attract a better type of student.

In running the laboratory services of several large hospitals, I have come in contact with graduates of many medical schools and have never been convinced that as far as the quality of the main product is concerned—namely, the abilities of its recent graduates—there is any very substantial difference in the standards of various schools. I have seen some, admittedly very few, complete deadheads who got through Harvard, which is generally regarded as the medical school with the greatest prestige. In fact a real deadhead Harvard graduate is in a class all by himself, far outranking in dumbness the poor-quality products of lesser schools. Their stupidity is not entirely unadorned. They seem to feel that the Harvard diploma makes up for all other deficiencies, and they become the most aggressively inadequate doctors in the field. On the other hand I have seen some topnotch doctors who were rejected by American medical schools and finally attended some obscure and second-rate European school.

I suppose I make the business of medical-school admission sound like an awful jungle. The plain truth of the matter is that any premedical student with a reasonable amount of poise, character and personality, with not too displeasing a personal appearance and a modest degree of scholastic attainment, has always been able to get into medical school without too much difficulty and even have considerable latitude in picking the school of his choice.

In my day things were simpler but more terrifying. There were no admission committees, no aptitude tests and no complicated and searching forms to fill out. A date was simply set for the premedical group to go over to the medical school en masse and be interviewed by the dean in person. We sat in a row on a bench in the foyer just outside the dean's office. The door was left open and as each candidate went in we could hear semi-audible questions the dean was delivering in a voice that fluctuated rapidly from a low, raucous bullfrog-like croak to a high-pitched whine as he rose to the assault. Naturally I was last in the row, and as each successive interviewee emerged red-faced and in a great sweat, my apprehension increased. As I inched along the bench to the threshold, the questioning became more audible and ominous. The student who was to go in just preceding me was a brassy type who was firmly convinced his success depended on his standing up to the withering interrogation.

By the time he went in, I was just outside the door and could hear the questions quite clearly, although I could not catch the responses. "Why do you want to be a doctor? What makes you think you would be a good doctor? What does your father do for a living? Why don't you go into the grocery business with him? Do you think you are better than your father? You mean you want to make a lot of money? Was your name always Stuart? Why did you change it?"—and so on, deadlier and deadlier. I wasn't feeling so good when it came my turn. When I went into the inquisitorial chamber I met a real Mussolini setup. The five-foot-five Mephistophelean dean was well submerged behind an enormous desk at the end of a large room that seemed a hundred feet long but was only forty when I measured it surreptitiously at a later date. My feet sank ankle-deep into a heavy rug as I trod across the room. Adjoining the dean was a secretary, who sat poised with a stenographic pad, obviously prepared to take down every grunt I made. A spotlight was directed, third-degree fashion, on the seat in which the student was to sit. I did the only thing any sensible person would in such a situation. I promptly swooned.

Days later, while I was reading a brochure on how to become a master plumber, a letter arrived informing me that I had been admitted to medical school. I assumed that this was some clerical error but wasn't going to press my luck by inquiring. I had the bona-fide acceptance in writing and the school would have to honor it. Later I learned that it was no error at all. The dean had been rather favorably impressed by his ability to make a student faint at sight and was therefore kindly disposed toward me. Still later, when my fellow-students chided me about the event, I claimed that the whole thing was a fake I had carefully planned in advance. So the aspiring medical-school applicant wants some inside dope from an old war horse like myself about how to get into medical school? All I can say is study like blazes, wear elevator heels on your shoes and carry a rabbit's foot in your pocket.

CHAPTER

12

My Enviable Friends
the Researchers

N o t too long ago, I had a depressing conversation
with the leading internist of a fairly large New England city, who was about to retire. He had been recognized for many years as the uncrowned head of the medical fraternity in his community. One could hardly think
of anyone who had been so useful a citizen, both in his
own large practice and in the high standards he had
set for younger doctors in the area. He had helped
many of them get established and enjoyed the esteem of
the medical profession and the public alike. You would
think that from his retirement he would be able to
look back on his career with satisfaction and a feeling
of fulfillment.

Yet he said to me, rather wistfully, that if he had his life to live over again, he would never have left the environment of his medical-school days. His greatest regret was that he had not devoted his career to research work. To me this was disheartening on several counts. In the first place, he could hardly have led a more rewarding life if he had been a researcher. I could easily think of a dozen research men, with modest attainments to their credit, whose combined efforts would not even begin to stack up against his own in terms of human benefit.

As a young doctor at Johns Hopkins, he had written a report describing a newly recognized disease entity. His name has ever since been attached to this rather rare condition, and I suppose this single youthful stroke now looms large in his own mind as an indication of what his career might have been. Perhaps most of us have some slight yearning for immortality in one fashion or another. But this doctor, I think, had beguiled himself. The memory of eminent researchers of the past may vanish as quickly, and sometimes more quickly, into oblivion than that of other doctors. My present crop of residents has never even heard of many of the researchers who were famous in my own youth. Many of the great names in the history of medicine belong to practitioners rather than to those remembered primarily for new discoveries.

I believe that my internist friend was also self-deceived about his probable achievement if he had pursued a research career, but of course I did not attempt to disillusion him. The chances are that if he had really had the divine spark leading to investigation, he would never have gone into practice at all, or would have been so unhappy at it that he would quickly have given it up. If he had become a researcher by rationalization rather than natural inclination, he would very likely have spent a frustrated and futile life performing fruitless experiments by the score. I regret to say that there are more than a few people in research laboratories who might be more usefully employed elsewhere. If at first you don't succeed, you had better think seriously of trying something else, heretical as this may sound. Although successful people like to tell about the trials and tribulations of their early days and how they persevered against all odds, the ones that I have known hit their own particular jackpot early in life and, in fact, sometimes had it thrust upon them.

My chief concern about the retiring clinician's reaction is that it points up very vividly one side effect of the present-day emphasis on the importance of medical research. It has resulted, unintentionally I suppose, in a downgrading of other kinds of medical talent. I could understand how, in the medical-school environment, those outside the magic research circle might acquire a feeling of inferiority. But to realize that this attitude had permeated throughout the medical field was disturbing.

Doctors on the staffs of so-called university hospitals, namely those closely affiliated with medical schools, have a threefold function. They must teach, they must participate in patient care and they usually carry on experimental projects of one sort or another. With the growing importance of research and the realization that prestige and chances for advancement depend increasingly upon success in this direction, the three functions have got out of balance. The gifted teacher and the competent bedside doctor often feel that they are playing second fiddle. The pathologist may begin to think that he and his microscope belong in the percussion section of the orchestra, necessary perhaps in their own specialized way, but only occasionally permitted to make a loud, clanging noise. There are unusually gifted persons who are talented in all three directions but these, in my experience, are rare, probably because somewhat different basic qualities are required in each sphere.

The combination of competent teacher and effective researcher, or of competent doctor and good teacher, is not too uncommon. But to have all three talents in one person is like hitting the "daily triple" at a race track if there were such a thing. The competent doctor is one who can utilize his medical knowledge in a highly efficient and practical way. The gifted teacher is one who can assimilate, organize and project other people's knowledge. The talented researcher is one who sees things in a different light from that of ordinary people. He does not accept conventional opinions without question but tends to make his own interpretations.

When he teaches, his original point of view may confuse rather than enlighten. The very topnotch researchers I have known have been, with few exceptions, rather miserable lecturers, at least compared to the pedagogical standards found in most undergraduate colleges. They may talk brilliantly about their own work or that of others in the same field, but they sometimes lack teaching versatility or the ability to project their own knowledge at the student level. There was a time when the ability to teach well was considered a primary qualification of medical-school faculty members. Nowadays it is classed as a very useful accomplishment but secondary in importance to research ability.

A medical-school faculty committee engaged in the sometimes trying task of selecting a new professor, and occasionally behaving like a pack of hounds pursuing an elusive fox, is seldom very much impressed if a prospective candidate is said to be a marvelous teacher. It is much more likely to be swayed by how many scientific papers he has published. The usual expression is that So-and-So "has" a hundred and sixty papers, or whatever his score may be. There is a story about one such committee that found itself unable to choose between two equally qualified prospects. Finally a secretary was asked to go through the past ten years of the Cumulative Medical Index, which compiles all medical writing, and make a bibliography for each contender. One of them was much larger and more varied in subject matter than the other, and the decision was made accordingly. Only later was it discovered that the successful candidate had a namesake working in the same field and had received bibliographical credit for the work of two.

I suppose it is grossly misleading to speak of the various facets of a doctor's ability as though they were distinct, uniform and measurable. I think I can recognize the natural investigator when I see him but I am still greatly mystified as to what makes him tick. One fairly common characteristic may be that he has what is sometimes pretentiously called a "dynamic" approach to unsolved problems. This distinguishes him sharply from the morphological pathologist, who is likely to be a very static thinker. When the researcher has occasion to look through our microscopes, he sees things happening. One kind of cell transforms itself into another, or an Aschoff body (a lesion found in rheumatic hearts) "thrusts itself" from one spot to another. Such presumed mobility in pieces of dead tissue seems in rather bad taste to old-fashioned pathologists.

Researchers tend to be amused at the antics of routine pathologists as they fool around with their silly old compound-light microscopes, but many lines of research do tend to lead back to cell or tissue structure. The day frequently arrives when the basic researcher wants to know what structural changes his investigative procedures have caused. He may impress his own usually very formidable-looking and expensive microscope into use and come up with some startling dynamic interpretations, or if he is more cautious by nature, he may seek counsel from a pathologist.

207

I once wasted a great deal of time examining the heart muscle of caterpillars that had been given one of the purest of bacterial poisons. The researcher was very impatient with me for my inability to find any real change, since he had devised a way of measuring the insect's electrocardiographic patterns, and these had been very abnormal. That is the usual story. Our findings seldom come up to the researchers' expectations and they go away with an even dimmer view of a pathologist's usefulness than they took before.

A pathologist approaches his microscopic interpretations in the manner of a professional golfer lining up an intricate putt. To the researcher such preliminary gymnastics are a trifle absurd. When he feels the urge to do his own microscopic evaluation, he steps up briskly and, without taking a stance, smacks the ball backhanded. It usually ends up on the other side of the green. But occasionally this casual technique scores a bull's-eye, and that really exasperates the pathologist.

Most of the routine pathologist's resentment toward the investigators is based on crystal-pure envy, as I have already pointed out. We sometimes have paranoid reactions and imagine that even when they say pleasant things to us, we are being patronized. Once, with a group of doctors, I attended the dedication exercises of a new hospital. We were taken on a tour of the plant and finally came to the autopsy room, which was situated, as is common nowadays, next to the morgue. When autopsies were considered of major importance, the autopsy room was usually placed as centrally in the hospital as the operating rooms. An ordinary, unguarded toilet bowl had been installed in the autopsy room for the disposal of waste materials. No one could question its usefulness but it did rather shatter the décor of the otherwise beautifully appointed suite of rooms. A very high-class researcher, one of the group of guests, roared with laughter when he saw the aforementioned object. "At last," he cried with joy, "I have found something useful in an autopsy room." I will never forgive or forget.

There is one circumstance that may lead the high-class researcher to treat the local pathologist as an equal and a worthy colleague—when he happens to discover some abnormal lump growing somewhere on his own anatomy. Then he will consult and plague us with all sorts of questions. He wants to know exactly what kind of lump this is. The precious little histological details that ordinarily bore him are now of absorbing interest. He wants to know just how the lump originated, whether the surgeon got it all out, what the chances of its growing back may be and whether in any way, no matter how remote, it is potentially malignant. He hangs on our every word and tells us everything about the lump that he can summon up. In fact, he behaves exactly as I do when I am sick and consult a clinician.

At first we are flattered by this unexpected attention, but before we can satisfy his curiosity completely we are often frankly bored. Nevertheless, we are pleased that he has at last discovered we pathologists serve a definite function and are useful people to have around.

Maybe, we think, he will treat us as equals and comrades from now on. Our expectations are doomed to disappointment. A few days later he has forgotten all about it and again we are assigned the role of spear-carriers.

Another reason for my peevishness toward research men is that they tend to rob us of our illustrious past by referring to famous pathologists of long ago as "investigators," not as routine pathologists who used the microscope as an investigative tool. A few years ago a very fine biography of William Welch was published. But the average reader of this book would not have got the impression that Dr. Welch was primarily a pathologist, who spent most of his career in the autopsy room or over the microscope, and that one of his major accomplishments was to train other pathologists who later became famous in their own right.

When pathologists first realized that their routine procedures were outmoded as primary or basic investigative techniques, many of them turned to newer methods and forsook the autopsy room. Young pathologists who were interested in a career in academic medicine were anxious to dissociate themselves from the dead carcass of routine pathology. Some succeeded admirably as investigators on their own, others collaborated with research-minded doctors in other departments of the medical school. Most of us, I regret to say, were too set in our ways to permit much adaptation.

The pathologists who were successful in other lines of investigation, with some notable exceptions, soon lost both their interest and proficiency in routine diagnostic pathology. There are still quite a few pathologists who have excellent reputations as experimenters and yet continue to supervise diagnostic pathological services. These will no doubt resent belligerently my implication that a sort of schism exists between their efforts as experimenters and as pathologists. The chimeras of this type whom I have known at close hand excelled in either one or the other category and hardly ever in both. They are like those two-headed Russian surgical dogs. The experimental head gets all the nourishment, the pathological one merely drools.

One of the primary qualifications of an investigator is that he must believe firmly in the validity of his methods and the potential significance of the work he is doing. This does not mean to imply that investigators are altogether free of moments when they become discouraged or critical about their own work—when experiments for which they had great hopes yield negative results or even cast doubt on the results of previous experiments. Many of the researchers I have known were highly moody people because of this. I once spent an afternoon harvesting a modest crop of apples at the country home of a very successful investigator. He was not in high spirits at the time, and when we had completed our chore, we drove to the nearest village and sold our harvest to the local grocer for a negligible sum. On the return ride my companion was singularly silent. Finally he confided, "You know, that is the first honest money I have ever earned."

Very often I invite investigators to give seminars in my own department. I do this because I don't want to get too much out of touch with what is cooking in the research laboratories, and I feel that the young men whose training in pathology I am responsible for should be advised of probable future developments in medicine. Naturally, I eschew the second-raters in favor of those whose studies have been productive and provocative. The atmosphere of a routine laboratory bristling with activity, with technicians hopping around trying to keep up with the never-ending demands of capricious residents, is likely to have a sobering effect on these investigators when they arrive. They sometimes say to me, "It must be wonderful to have a job with well-defined duties and with many people depending on your services." This is, of course, a transient reaction, but they do not say this merely to console me for my fall from scientific grace.

After they have concluded their seminars, knowing they captured the attention of their audience, their self-assurance returns. In some ways the blackboard in the seminar room is the equivalent of the psychiatrist's famous couch. I think this is the reason why researchers seldom refuse to present their data, even if it means a great deal of inconvenience to them and even if they receive no compensation—financially, that is. Often the same material is presented over and over again to many different and sometimes inconsequential groups. The researcher is not looking for recognition, in the ordinary self-advertising sense of the word. He needs periodically repeated assurances that his work is not sterile and not without interest to others. The chalk-drawn percentage-distribution curve is his rainbow. The presentations he makes to groups of other researchers may be challenging in the sense that his efforts will be carefully scrutinized and questioned, but the interest of such research-minded groups can be more or less taken for granted. In a way, it is much more satisfying to captivate a group of doctors who are not research-oriented.

Up to now I have been writing exclusively about the large body of reputable and able medical investigators because these are the ones I know best. But the glamour and prestige of medical research work have become so great that a large number of hangers-on, whose motives are somewhat suspect, have been attracted to the field. Many of them are no better equipped than I am to perform investigations, but they love the climate in which research work is performed and like to identify themselves with it. They bask in the reflected glory of other men's accomplishments, and prefer to do chiefly imitative or repetitive types of experiments. They probably wouldn't recognize an important incidental finding if they came upon one by accident.

Even in the long lean years of the depression there was such a thing as a "research bum." He would spend most of each year trying to secure grants to support himself the following year, and hardly had time enough to conduct any new experiments. Some of these misguided anomalies were rather pathetic. They lived a harassed life until a last-minute reprieve in the form of a new grant kept them going for yet another year. But the new deluge of research money from all sorts of sources has changed all that. Even researchers of dubious distinction now pursue their careers in relative opulence.

It would be a most unfortunate state of affairs if sufficient funds were not available for well-qualified investigators to carry on their work. Furthermore, no one really has the right to decide who is or isn't qualified. The prevailing opinion is that almost anyone who wants to do experimental work should be encouraged. I have no quarrel with that, but the current philosophy that good research is a purchasable commodity, like the wares in a delicatessen showcase, has a fallacious aspect to it. It would be a difficult thing to prove that beyond a certain point the easy accessibility of research funds has produced an increased volume of important contributions. Good poetry can be written just as well in a barren attic as in a palace. It is distressing even to contemplate the amount of indifferent verse that would be produced if grants were as available to poets as they are to medical experimenters. Important medical discoveries have a way of coming from backwater kitchen-type laboratories almost as often as they do from the large scientific cathedrals.

I have always held the private opinion that if a planned research project is the kind for which financial support can be readily enlisted from various foundations, it is probably so conventional and orthodox that it is doomed to insignificance from the start. Officials of various grant-giving institutions would take violent exception to this point of view, overtly at least. But the fact that most grants of this type usually specify that the recipient need not stick too closely to the experimental procedures outlined in their applications is almost tacit admission that the investigator may want to try out some ideas that might sound weird if put into writing.

The boom in medical research has been greatly souped up by the constant barrage of stories in newspapers and magazines about hot-off-the-griddle discoveries. These create the impression that hardly a week passes but that some major disease has bit the dust. They also support the notion that the increased volume of discoveries is the direct result of the greater availability of research money. The question may be raised of how authentic many of these premature releases prove ultimately to be and whether they do more harm than good.

There was a time when an investigator might be greatly embarrassed if his work in progress was reported in the press, but this feeling seems long since to have disappeared. Some experimenters even seem to covet such publicity. Nevertheless, there are still many occasions when he is unhappy about the way his work has been interpreted. The substance of the item may be reasonably accurate, but the headline that adorns it can be traumatic. Researchers put up with or encourage these press releases because they know it helps make money available for further investigations.

I generally glance at the headlines of these almost daily newspaper stories but seldom have the fortitude to read them all the way through. A librarian at the medical school once decided to clip all these reports and file them by subject matter. All the impending cures for cancer, arthritis, peptic ulcer or heart disease, as well as all the revelations about the fundamental nature of life, were stored away, each in its proper folder. On one occasion I went through her formidable collection and it was at once obvious that when all the items in each category were read together, they seemed pretentious and even a trifle absurd in the light of subsequent developments.

A great deal of medical news of this nature is obtained by "science writers" who attend large meetings of medical organizations at which preliminary reports of work in progress are the bulk of the scientific program. These reports are often made for the understandable, if not altogether commendable, motive of obtaining priority for a brand-new and often incompletely tested observation. They are also made for the much more valid motive of comparing notes with other investigators. The reporter is the intruder in the midst who too easily translates tentative conclusions into certainties. He may protest that he always clears his facts with the investigator but the latter is only human and may secretly have no objection to seeing his name in the papers.

Many of these preliminary reports are followed months later by a detailed publication in which the tentative conclusions are considerably modified or toned down. In other cases, further work invalidates the interpretation of the original report, and all that ever appears is a brief abstract in the proceedings of the meeting. Meanwhile, by his overeagerness to present the story to the public, the reporter has in fact distorted it. A patient with a chronic disease may read of some newly discovered miracle cure for his own ailment and ask his doctor to give him the new treatment. If he has faith in his doctor he will accept his explanation that the value and hazards of the new cure have yet to be established. Nevertheless the patient may have a lingering suspicion that his doctor is behind the times.

Pathologists, except for the specialized medical-examiners faction, do not as a rule have much traffic with newspapermen. But the latter have painted the picture of the researchers as the fairest flowers in all medical horticulture, and it follows logically that we pathologists are only the weeds. Therefore I bear them a grudge that I shall presently try to settle.

13

Our Friends the Journalists, No Enemies Needed

T H E busy telephone rings yet again. I am relieved, however, that this time it is not a disgruntled resident. I hear a cultivated voice that obviously belongs to a recent girl graduate. Old gaffer that I am, I cannot spot whether it is Bryn Mawr or Radcliffe, but it has decided undertones of Brearley or Spence. She confides that she is a researcher on a picture magazine (even the homework of high-school students is now called research) and that she is working on a story about experimental arteriosclerosis in baboons. She has heard that some investigators in Texas have been concerned with this problem and has been told that I am just the man who can tell her all about it. A little questioning reveals that she is on a chain-reaction buggy ride and I am the sixth person in the chain. Each of the previous people has given her the name of a new victim with whom he is settling an old score.

She says, "It would make such a cute story, what with pictures of the baboons and all."

I reply, "Wouldn't you rather get married instead?"

"All in good time, but right now I am interested in ordinary baboons."

I tell her that arteriosclerosis is the dullest, dreariest and, nongeometrically, the squarest of all diseases and that her use of the word "cute" is ill-advised. To which she responds, "Oh, dear, you aren't being any help at all." By this time I have selected No. 7 in the chain, from a group of likely prospects. I tell her that he is just her man but she will have to be insistent and pump him real hard because he is a little shy. Whether the story ever appeared or not, I do not know. My barber subscribes only to *Esquire.*

On another occasion the school authorities advised me that a picture magazine had made arrangements to take photographs at the hospital in connection with a feature story about rheumatoid arthritis. My part was to see that the photographer attended a minor operation in which a small lump was to be removed from the elbow of a patient with this disease. Such lumps are very distinctive in appearance under the microscope and are often removed for examination, although in themselves they are quite harmless.

This incident happened around the time cortisone

was first used to treat this kind of arthritis. There had been considerable publicity about it, and this was the reason the proposed feature story was considered timely. Arthritis specialists were then keenly interested in what cortisone might do to the appearance of such lumps, since they did not readily melt away under treatment, even though the patient often felt much better. On the scheduled day, a thin, bespectacled youngster, with an enormous amount of photographic gear hanging from his shoulders and filling both arms, arrived at the laboratory. I took him to be the photographer's caddie and said, "Sonny, when will your boss be along? He's late." He replied indignantly in a high-pitched, squeaky voice, "I'm the boss." This surprised me because I had always thought of big-time picture magazine photographers as swashbuckling, derring-do adventurers. I asked him if he had ever been in an operating room before and he replied, "No, but I'm just dying to see an operation."

I escorted him to one of the smaller operating rooms, where the lump was to be removed under local anesthesia. After all, it was a very minor procedure requiring just a small superficial cut in the skin—the whole business would probably last only a few minutes. I helped him get his equipment set up and found a surgeon's green monkey suit small enough to fit him. It looked rather well on him, in an outlandishly incongruous way.

Finally the surgeon arrived—a very junior resident, since this was such a simple procedure. The patient proved to be very talkative, offering helpful suggestions throughout the operation. "Cortisone is wonderful," he said, "but taking these lumps out is what really does the job." Patients are quite remarkable that way. Give one of them a special drug to relieve difficulty in breathing and the next week he is back demanding more of the same. "Makes me move my bowels regularly," he'll say, not too confidentially. "Doesn't it help you breathe more easily?" the exasperated doctor will ask. "Why, no," the surprised patient will reply. "Was it supposed to?" That's why I'm a pathologist.

I told the photographer to stand in back of me and I would signal him when the lump was exposed enough for him to get a good view. Then I would duck out of the way and he could take his shots. When the proper moment arrived, I turned around—the photographer was flat on his face. He had passed out cold, and science had suffered another setback.

My other contacts with members of the press have been limited but I remember them vividly. Many years ago the school I was associated with launched a campaign to raise badly needed funds. As part of this program, an arrangement was made with a local newspaper to publish a series of feature articles that would dramatize the accomplishments of each department of the school. A rather hard-boiled representative of the paper spent a whole day talking to each member of our department. He took voluminous notes but it was easy to see his frustration intensify as he failed to obtain any quotable information from any of us. Toward the end of the day one of the part-time members of the department, whose plans for future work were always impressive but who never really spent any time in the laboratory, happened by and entered into conversation with the feature writer.

The latter was immediately transformed. Almost everything our part-time staff member had to say was a good lead for a story. You could almost see the writer, with a great sigh of relief, clearing the decks in his mind and starting all over again. He gave the rest of us a look of undisguised disdain and said unabashedly, "Now we're getting somewhere." When the story finally appeared, practically all of it had to do with the slightly imaginary research activities of our hanger-on staff member but it was a very good story. It was this incident that made me realize how large a gap exists between the needs of news reporters and the aims of laboratory workers.

Years later I wrote a paper in which I tried to show, with the aid of some rather dubious statistics, that heavy drinkers were as vulnerable to "hardening" of the arteries as total abstainers. It had not occurred to me that this was a newsworthy item, but some press service promptly picked it up and it went out on the wires under the heading, DOCTOR SAYS IT'S O.K. TO TAKE THAT EXTRA DRINK. It was obvious that the press wasn't much interested in making an accurate appraisal of the findings, one way or the other. It had merely come across an item that had reader interest. For several months thereafter, I sporadically received letters from newspaper readers throughout the country and realized that the item was being used as a filler whenever a column ran a bit short.

Very recently, more or less by accident, I became one of a group of doctors who were to form the panel at a discussion of the causes of heart attacks. About a week or so before we met, I received a wire from the public-relations officer of the organization sponsoring it, stating that representatives of the press wished to have a group conference with the doctors after the discussion was over. I was to inform him immediately whether or not I was willing to participate. I neglected to reply and several days later received a telephone call from the public-relations man, who let me know in no uncertain terms that it was extremely naughty of me not to have replied at once. In fact, he seemed a little perturbed that a pathologist was on the panel at all. I agreed to attend the press conference, not because I had any message to divulge to the public but because I was curious about the way such conferences are conducted.

At the meeting, a group of about fifteen writers confronted our group of about nine doctors and began asking rather vague questions and receiving equally vague answers. Every time any doctor said something that sounded the least bit novel or provocative, some other doctor disagreed and the first one promptly withdrew or modified his original statement. It was soon clear that nothing newsworthy was likely to materialize from this group interview, for the simple reason that there wasn't any story to be told. No really important discovery had been made about the subject under discussion since about 1913. And yet if the reporters had been interviewing the doctors individually, they might well have got them to say incautious things that could have been built into intriguing news items, such as one about the virtues of eating sardines for breakfast.

As the stalemate became more evident, one of the reporters complained that they had not been given any message for their readers. At this point one of the doctors suggested that the newspapers ought to grant a "moratorium of five years" before publishing any further news items on this particular subject. I agreed wholeheartedly with this suggestion and would have set the period at fifteen years at least. But it did not seem the most propitious moment to propose this. My colleague's suggestion met with icy silence. To twist the knife a bit in the wound, the doctor went on to say, "You should see how wonderfully the press in England handles medical-science news."

This was a little too much for one particularly irate reporter in the front row who responded with "Say, doctor, we didn't ask for this interview. We were invited here and told that you wanted a news release that would help your organization raise money." The meeting broke up very rapidly thereafter, although a bespectacled lady reporter pursued me to the front door still angling for a story. By chance, I rode back to town in the same bus with the irate reporter, who berated medical researchers all the way. He shook a bunch of loose notepaper at me and said, "Look at this junk. There isn't the trace of a story in it. Who do you doctors think you are and where do you get off telling us how to do our jobs?" I was not at all surprised to find nothing about the meeting in the papers next day. A journalist friend of mine, when he heard about the incident, said, "You were just a bunch of amateurs. Every one of you should have had prepared handouts in your pockets to distribute to each reporter present."

There are all sorts of harmful addictions besides the use of narcotics. My own particular weakness is for heavy-handed sarcasm. Since nothing is so calculated to strain the affection of your associates, I constantly strive to kick the habit, but with only limited success. When the provocation is great enough, I relapse. For example, when one of my residents breaks forth with some high-flown speculations about medical theory, I release my biggest gun and say, "Did you read that in a newspaper?" This is delivered with a broad sneer and never fails to deflate the most aggressive expounder of doubtful information.

Medical writers are undoubtedly sincere, competent and experienced journalists. They know their jobs, which is basically the writing of stories that will interest their readers. Nor do I not question their honesty or reliability. They report the facts as they were given to them. One doesn't often see a medical news item that contains gross misstatements. But the interpretation of the facts and the emphasis they are given often create misleading or exaggerated impressions.

In effect, the journalists try to make spot news out of medical reports as rapidly as they appear. "Next week's issue of *Lancet* will say . . ." is not an uncommon opening for medical news items these days. But the accretion of new medical knowledge is a slow and tortuous process with more wild swings than blows that land. It is a process that requires considerable proving and testing by more than one group of investigators. In a scientific publication the author presents his data in the main body of the article. It is only in the section called "discussion" that he permits himself to indulge in some cautious speculation about the implications and possible applications of the data. When a journalist translates such information into a news story, it is the potential value of the data that captures his attention and flavors his product. That is why so many impending discoveries announced in the public press either never materialize or are doomed to a short life span. To avoid being accused of making a sweeping generalization, I shall mention the present status of some hopeful "discoveries" of yesteryear that were once publicly clarioned.

Artificial pneumothorax never became much of a cure for lobar pneumonia. Biotin has never prevented cancer from developing in anyone. Cytotoxic antisera have never cured cancer or, for that matter, leukemia. Rutin did not turn out to be a preventive of high blood pressure. It is doubtful that any anticancer chemical has been discovered that will destroy tumor tissue without doing the same to normal bone marrow. Transplants of organs from man to man have still been successful only in identical twins, with possibly one or two exceptions. Hardly anyone any longer believes that lipotropic agents prevent arteriosclerosis. Heparin probably doesn't work either. The sulfhydryl group of chemicals has not solved the mysteries of the origin of life. The rice diet for hypertension no longer enjoys the wide acceptance it had initially. Practically no one tries to dissolve blood clots with trypsin nowadays. I haven't seen a pulmonary embolectomy set in years.

I could go on almost indefinitely. In most instances it was not the doctors advancing these ideas who made exaggerated claims for them but the news releases, which made them sound like almost sure things. Medical researchers have never claimed to be infallible. I doubt that there are many experienced investigators who have not somewhere written or said something that they wish they could retract. After all, the great John Hunter introduced syphilis into high society with his skin scarifications. Koch's experiments with tuberculin as an immunizing agent helped make George Bernard Shaw antagonistic toward the medical profession. Ehrlich's famous 606 doesn't seem quite so miraculous in the light of present-day antibiotics. Any Listerite who tried to spray carbolic acid around in a modern operating room would be promptly thrown out.

One seldom sees puffed-up claims that prove to be of only transient glory reported in the syndicated health columns of doctors who write for the press. These are generally models of restraint and caution. They are also frequently unspectacular, for the same reason. Journalists who specialize in medical news writing have picked up quite a bit of knowledge about their subject, but they generally lack the background to evaluate medical claims judiciously. Research methods and techniques have become so complicated that even a well-trained physician may be unable to analyze or interpret the results reported in many publications. I admire the ease and confidence with which the science writers simplify and clarify the most involved research projects, although I don't always accept their versions. In fact, it is no easy matter to determine the significance of investigative work when it first appears.

When I was young, I once belonged to a journal club in which I was expected to report on recent advances in the field of pathology. One of the journals I covered was the "obscure" British *Journal of Experimental Pathology*. In it, from time to time, I came across articles about a mold that would prevent bacteria from growing on agar plates. "Whatever will these droll bacteriologists think of next?" I said to myself as I ignored these articles in favor of those dealing with road dust and cancer of the lung. I need hardly mention the name of the author whose articles I was ignoring. Perhaps I have the instincts of a journalist myself.

I don't suppose that extravagant medical news reports really cause much harm, and I doubt that the average reader recalls yesterday's profound medical revelation. Moreover, the medical items at least represent a relief from the large amount of unpleasant news about crime and violence that fills a good portion of the newspaper. My biggest complaint, however, is that the journalists have created a somewhat fictitious world of medical scientific accomplishment. The average person must believe that the medical-research laboratories are full of inspired geniuses who, if they were only given enough financial support, would solve all the problems of human illness in short order. A news item will suggest that a cure for cancer is just around the corner, but meanwhile the pathologist faces an increasing amount of it, and it shows no sign of waning. Early diagnosis, says another news item, will practically eliminate death from any form of disease. An ounce of prevention is worth a pound of cure, it proclaims most wittily. What the article neglects to say is that many diseases cannot be detected until they cause symptoms, by which time they are often incurable.

I have no doubt that the abundant publicity enhances the prestige of the researchers and makes it easier to raise money for research purposes. The capable investigators can use the money, but they hardly need the plaudits of the public. As the status of the researcher increases, that of other groups in the medical community, by contrast, declines. When socialized medicine makes its almost inevitable appearance and the medical administrators become the overlords of the profession, the bedside doctor and the routine pathologist will be further downgraded to the level of tradesmen. It will be interesting to see what quality of student will choose to become a practicing doctor in such circumstances and whether the next generation will have as much confidence in its doctors as the present one does.

14

═══════════

Final Note

T H E social success of ants and other insects, the entomologists tell us, is due to the fact that they move at a constant rate of locomotion, which varies only with the temperature. They are equally unable to elude an antagonistic brother insect or to overtake a reluctant inamorata. Autopsy-performing pathologists are a bit like ants. We have been moving around at a constant rate of speed for a long time. But lately the climate has been changing, and one day in the not-too-distant future we may end up by becoming medically lyophilized. The omens and portents are already with us.

Several years ago an influential internist wrote a disturbing lead editorial for the *Journal of the American*

Medical Association in which he raised the question whether autopsies performed in their time-honored manner had not outlived their usefulness. To most pathologists this editorial came as something of a major shock. Many of us had heard the same opinion expressed privately by other temporarily disgruntled clinicians, but usually without too much conviction or sincerity. For the first time the value of autopsies had been challenged in the official organ of the medical profession and in an authoritative way.

In the following weeks a sizable number of letters of protest and rebuttal from pathologists were published and I suspect an even larger number were received. It seemed to me that the arguments offered by the pathologists were tepid and ineffective. The autopsy-dishonoring clinician clearly remained the victor. Many clinicians of my acquaintance did not agree with the premise of the original editorial. But I was disheartened to find that not one of them was sufficiently aroused to add his voice to the protests of the disaffected pathologists.

The position of the pathologists, in my opinion, was untenable because they simply denied the main point of the editorial. They did not refute it with facts, because the truth of the matter is that the clinician's charges were valid. His chief contention was that no great medical discoveries are likely to be made by continuing the systematic performance of autopsies in the accustomed manner, and any pathologist who denies the truth of this is merely deluding himself. He is in the position of the movie mogul who refuses to accept the fact that television has hurt him and his main product. The pathologist who insists that autopsies "are as good as ever" is not facing the facts. He would be on much safer ground if he claimed that autopsies are good for the public weal, but then he would be treating one aspect of the function of autopsies that is seldom aired and is in fact almost taboo.

Nothing much happened after the publication of this editorial. Pathologists, at least in teaching hospitals, continued to do more and more autopsies for smaller and smaller audiences that showed less and less interest. About a year ago I attended a dinner at which only pathologists were present. It preceded a scientific meeting of a local pathological society. One member of the dinner party had just returned from a committee meeting in Washington of nationally known pathologists, and told us all about it. (In medical circles a committee dropper outranks a name dropper.)

At the Washington meeting the subject of the usefulness of autopsies had cropped up and monopolized the conversation, although it had not been on the original agenda. About half the committee took the position that autopsies had become pretty much outmoded and were consuming too much time that might more gainfully be spent in carrying out investigations and other pursuits. These pathologists were of the opinion that they ought to have the right to decide whether or not any particular autopsy should be done. After examining the clinical records and consulting with the clinicians, they should have the authority to say whether or not the autopsy held sufficient interest for it to be performed. The group at our dinner immediately became embroiled in the same argument. Since most of us were working pathologists and not influential policy-makers, we felt that the proposed selection of autopsies was an outrage against our traditions.

The government committee member was a pathologist of my own vintage and background who one would have supposed might favor the preservation of the status quo. Yet he sided with the radical group at Washington. I felt he was being a traitor and proceeded to call him Benedict Arnold for the rest of the evening. My own contention that pathologists have a duty and obligation to perform autopsies, regardless of their scientific merit, in order to check up on the accuracy of clinical diagnosis and thus serve the public was unanimously howled down. I was told that I was raising an ethical question that didn't exist, and that in each case it was up to the conscience of the attending physicians to decide whether they thought it necessary to check up on their own diagnoses. They had not, they insisted vigorously, become pathologists in order to snoop or spy on clinicians.

I realized that it was wiser to keep the peace. Later on, the more I thought about it the more I realized that as a self-appointed champion of the public good I was violating one of the tenets of my own auric rule. This, succinctly stated, is, "Never do good unto others who would rather you didn't." The only hitch in this reasoning is that because of the mystery surrounding the performance of autopsies, the general public has little idea that one of their purposes is to prove the reliability and test the quality of medical care. Herein lies the message of this book. It is, in effect, an announcement published in the public-notices column of a newspaper saying, "My wife Elizabeth having left my bed and board, I will henceforth perform no more autopsies." I doubt that such notices do much damage to the credit standing of the various Elizabeths but at least the responsible parties have made their intentions clear.

I may have piled digression upon digression in order to establish the atmosphere in which pathologists work, what their duties are and how they get on with various associates. I have brought to bear a highly biased and icteric eye on the medical scene, at least as it appears in the environment of a hospital. It may be a very opinionated picture, but I hope it is a more realistic and even truthful one than can be obtained from the fictionalized accounts in which the doctor usually plays the role of a hero devoid of all sin and frailty or, more rarely, a villain with a few redeeming qualities. Doctors are quite ordinary persons conspicuously ennobled by the fact that they do so much for ailing people, slightly debased because they accept money for it, and occasionally debunked by some hypercritical pathologist.

I have portrayed the setting of the pathologist so that some small enlightened fragment of the public can judge for itself whether autopsies serve a useful purpose. I have no illusions that any sizable segment will

care one way or the other. But it seems to me that the
ultimate decision about the fate of autopsies should not
rest entirely with groups of doctors representing con-
flicting points of view.

One day recently, some messengers came to the laboratory from the main office of the hospital with autopsy-
consent slips for four patients, all of whom had died of
cancer of the lung. It was too much of a good thing,
even for an old autopsy fancier like myself. Not a single
clinician or resident put in an appearance at any of the
four autopsies, which were done more or less simultane-
ously. I have therefore, quite abruptly, changed my al-
legiance and have joined the ranks of Benedict Arnold.
Enough is enough.

It is now my considered opinion that if no one in particular cares to have an autopsy performed, there is no
reason in the world why it should be done. If the sur-
viving relatives are indifferent, if the attending physicians are not interested enough to visit the autopsy
room and if the pathologist, who has to do the work,
feels he will learn practically nothing, why should it be
done at all? Just to pay homage and make a sort of
human sacrifice to an artificially perpetuated fetish for
a high autopsy-percentage rate? I think this is an in-
sufficient reason. Conversations with other pathologists
make it abundantly clear that this is almost a universal
situation and not a local problem peculiar to any one
hospital.

If any of the three interested parties concerned ex-
presses a desire to have the autopsy done, then it should

be performed. Otherwise it should be omitted. The only qualification I would make is that relatives should be given a better idea of what is involved. The service I now supervise performed about five hundred autopsies last year. Under present conditions about two hundred of these could have been skipped as far as usefulness is concerned. No one learned very much from them and no one cared what was found.

I have written here that autopsies are a fascinating pursuit and that I never cease to find them stimulating. I do not retract this statement. I just don't like to work out four puzzles at the same time or even in rapid succession. If the solutions meant anything to anyone, that would be a quite different matter. I feel I could learn much more and teach my residents much more if I were not faced with the ever-growing glut of autopsies that mean nothing to anyone except perhaps some administrator who takes satisfaction in a high autopsy rate.

Poor hospitals generally have low, and good ones high, autopsy-percentage rates, but it does not necessarily follow that all hospitals with high rates are good ones. This peculiar statistic does not indicate the degree of interest that clinicians take in the autopsy findings of their own cases. In other words an increasing amount of humbug is involved. It is not the autopsy that should be discontinued, it is the nonsense connected with autopsy-percentage rates.

Hospital administrators are intensely interested in the quality of medical care provided by their own insti-

tutions. In publications devoted to hospital management, articles on how to evaluate such care frequently
appear. The titles of some of these articles are self-
revelatory. They include "Hospital Statistics Can't
Tell the Truth," "Who Should Do Surgery?" "The
Medical Audit Should Not Imply Punishment," "Audit
Shows Hospitals Where They Stand" and "Did They
Have Pneumonia or Didn't They?" Anyone who feels
I have been too outspoken in my criticism of the medical
profession is advised to read such articles if he wants to
see what inflammatory strictures of this nature can
really be like.

I find these reports disappointing not only because
they minimize the importance of pathology in "audit-
ing" hospital care, but because they are replete with the
adjectivized nouns and verbalized adjectives of good
old administrative writing. The consensus of most of
them is that no good method for judging the quality of
hospital medical care has as yet been devised. The administrators, whether converted businessmen or back-
slid doctors, depend heavily on statistics, and this probably explains their interest in high autopsy-percentage
rates.

Long exposure has made me distrustful of all medical statistics unless they prove something that sounds
reasonable to begin with. Somehow when a really substantial contribution is made to medical science, statistics proving its soundness are usually superfluous. I
once watched in fascination as a statistician proved conclusively, with the aid of elaborate figures, that cigarette

smoking causes cancer of the lung. The thing that fascinated me was that he chain-smoked incessantly as he gave his hour-long talk, lighting each new one from the stub of the old.

The most impressive statistics are the ones that prove that the life span of man is continuously expanding. When I first started performing autopsies some thirty years ago, the majority of the persons I examined were in their sixties. Since then a lot of impressive statistics have washed over the dam, not to mention an imposing array of life-saving medical discoveries. And in the year 1960 the majority of persons examined at autopsy are still in their sixties. Fewer people may die at a younger age and many more survive beyond this decade, but the sixties still sees the end of the largest number of us. If anyone doubts my word, I suggest that he tabulate the ages of the dead reported in the obituary columns of newspapers for a few days. And if he doesn't believe them, he should remember that the highly solvent insurance companies still accept sixty-five as the critical year, whether they sell you life insurance or a retirement annuity. In spite of all the wonderful advances in medical science, we still have a little way to go before we recover the biblical allotment of threescore and ten.

Medical research may produce marvelous new discoveries at a dizzy pace but these occur for the most part within the confines of well-charted mine fields of exploration. They are usually elaborations, variations or off-shoots of older and familiar discoveries. The new discoveries do not revolutionize our concepts as Virchow did when he established a firm basis for the idea of organic disease or Pasteur when he proved the infectious nature of certain varieties of microorganisms. Medical textbooks written only a short time before either of these two colossi of medicine did their work became hopelessly outmoded in rapid fashion. They are filled with expressions like "ill humours" and "miasmatic effluvias" and go on endlessly about all sorts of strange fevers. The textbooks written thirty years ago, however, are still sound. Their basic concepts are the same as those accepted today. They may not contain as large an amount of new information as the newer textbooks and their emphasis may be differently directed, but they are still very understandable.

This may sound like rank heresy to devotees of the daily medical revelation as reported in their newspapers or to the medically operatic glycerides of television. Research may have brought us quite a way in our understanding of disease, but it is as nothing compared to the distance that has yet to be traveled. Among the most commonly used words in the doctor's vocabulary are "idiopathic," "agnogenic," "essential" and "primary." These are merely convenient ways of saying, "It is not known."

About twenty years ago a physiologist advised me to toss my microscope into the wastepaper basket and construct or purchase a Warburg tissue respiratory apparatus. Such instruments are used to measure the oxygen consumption or carbon-dioxide production of isolated living cells. The physiologist assured me that in no time at all diseases would be classified not by what was to be seen under the microscope but by the type of respiration various tissues show under different conditions. Since then the Warburg apparatus and its many modifications have become streamlined and, like most modern medical appliances, things of beauty. But they stand in a corner of well-equipped experimental laboratories and are only occasionally put into use to prove some relatively minor point. They are still a research instrument without much clinical application. The compound microscope has outlasted it.

I believe it is the realization that some new revolutionary technique is required to open up new vistas of medical research that has led so many enthusiasts into the field of electron microscopy. I would concentrate on this new technique myself if I were younger. Up to now the revelations of this still new instrument have not been earth-shaking except perhaps in the study of viruses that are invisible under the old light microscope. The electron microscope yields magnifications that are forty to fifty times greater than is possible with the pathologist's old instrument, but structures seen in this fashion have a fossilized look. Thus far the electron microscope has succeeded in proving that big cell granules have little cell granules floating around inside 'em and that little ones have lesser ones, and so ad infinitum, to paraphrase an old ditty that used to poke fun at microscopists. But the day such an instrument can lay bare, in visible form, the wonders of the molecular structure of tissues—that will be the time to toss the old microscope and all the old textbooks out the window, in the hope that they will land on some appropriate resident. It is my fond hope and expectation that on that happy day of deliverance the doctors will be back in droves in the dissecting rooms, eager once again to learn the new, more finely textured morphology.

I have had many unpleasant things to say about my friends the doctors, and not very many nice things. This does not represent the whole of my feelings in the matter. It is just unfortunate that the purposes of this book have made it necessary to stress their deficiencies rather than their accomplishments. The world of medicine is a wonderful estate with many noble edifices of achievement and marvelously landscaped gardens and terraces of performance. It is all the result of centuries of accumulated knowledge that makes the present generation of medical man a most bountiful benefactor of his fellow man when he falls on days of illness. It would be foolish to pretend otherwise.

But behind this marvelous scene, and quite invisible to the rest of the world, is a small but untidy jungle in which I, as an autopsy pathologist, reside and labor. In it is to be found a conglomeration of the errors and mishaps that have been committed. It is part of my job to keep this jungle as small and inconspicuous as possible. Some doctors may say, "Let us abolish this jungle by pretending it doesn't exist and the simplest way to do this is to abolish the duties of the autopsy pathologist." They are wrong. The jungle will still exist and if the pathologist isn't there to mind it, it may spread beyond its present limited quarters.

As a pathologist I do not have much contact with the great everyday achievements of my practicing friends. I know that they relieve an enormous amount of misery and suffering and that they save countless lives. I see only the small number of their inevitable failures and this constant exposure to the futile, imperfect side of medicine makes me overpessimistic and cynical. It has strongly influenced and colored the point of view from which this book has been written. A pathologist working in a fair-sized or large hospital will perform or supervise from one to three autopsies daily. This may represent less than three per cent of the patients, obviously a tiny segment of the people treated in the hospital as a whole. But this small fraction by itself looms large to the more or less isolated pathologist who deals almost exclusively with it.

I am not in the least ashamed of my calling. I'm rather proud of it, and I have no feeling that my life has been wasted. I am firmly convinced that when I die I will give off the same unforgettable aroma as Dostoevski's saintly priest. In future reincarnations I shall doubtless suffer the inevitable fate of all pathologists and be transformed successively into a succession of disagreeable animal forms, but one day I will return to earth as a man and make a beeline for the nearest medical school and, amply fortified with smelling salts, seek admission.

If I have developed a flair for sporting leather elbow

patches on my tweed jacket, I shall become a research man. If I can manage a certain misty look in my eye, I shall become a surgeon, and if I have overcome my aversion to the complaints of sick people, I shall become an internist. Barring any of these accomplishments, and I doubt that even a reincarnation will make me achieve them, I shall become a lowly pathologist all over again.

What a marvelous new saltless medical utopia that will be for a pathologist to dehisce. Life expectancy will be a Methuselah-like seven hundred years. Everyone will receive a mélange of deliciously flavored vaccines by any route of their choice. Our drinking water will be enriched with a vast assortment of vital ingredients and everyone will be safely anticoagulated from birth. I can hardly wait to peek beneath that future shroud.

Addendum

T H I S book has been read in manuscript by a number
of doctors and has provoked strong reactions of varying
intensity. Several with writing aspirations of their own
have condemned it from beginning to end and claim that
I have been particularly unfair to pathologists. I hadn't
realized that they loved us so well. In other doctors it
has produced unexpected reactions. A surgeon said I
was too easy on surgeons, but should not have been so
severe with the poor internists and researchers. An internist thought I was too gentle with internists, but
should not have abused the researchers or surgeons. A
researcher was disappointed that I had not "poured it
on the researchers" but claimed I was too harsh to clinicians. You can't please everyone.

They agree unanimously that I have been too brutal

toward residents. The book has not been previewed by a resident. It seemed unwise to take chances with the spare copy. To the resident who feels he has been unreasonably used, I can only say that one day he may change his mind.